THE SOURCES OF LOVE AND FEAR

THE SOURCES OF LOVE AND FEAR

By

M. BEVAN - BROWN

B.A. (N.Z.), M.A. (Cantab.), M.B., Ch.B. (N.Z.)

With contributions by members of the
Christchurch Psychological Society

including

R. S. ALLAN, D.Sc., Ph.D., and
ENID F. COOK, M.B., Ch.B., D.P.H.

56484

NEW YORK

THE VANGUARD PRESS, INC.

ACKNOWLEDGMENTS

I wish to record my indebtedness to my colleagues at Cranmer House Clinic, without whose encouragement this book would not have been written. Also I should record my debt to those who encouraged and inspired me in earlier years in London, particularly Professor John Macmurray, Dr. H. Crichton-Miller, Dr. J. A. Hadfield and Dr. Millais Culpin.

M. BEVAN-BROWN

Christchurch, N.Z.
December 1948

CONTENTS

CONTENTS

PREFACE

BEFORE assessing the value of a book on an important topic, which deals with fundamentally new considerations at variance with, and even in defiance of orthodox conceptions, it is prudent to consider the qualifications of the author for his task.

Dr. Bevan-Brown has had extensive experience as a psychiatrist both in England and in New Zealand. In England, besides being engaged in private practice in Harley Street (London), he was Physician at the Tavistock Clinic for 17 years from the earlier pioneering days. He has held many appointments in his specialty and was for two years Chairman of the Medical Society of Individual Psychology, London.

His association over a period of years with such men as Jung, Adler, Stekel, McDougall, William Brown, Edward Glover, Crichton-Miller, Suttie and Hadfield, has given him a wide knowledge of the various schools. His attitude towards psychological theory and practice is basically Freudian; and I think he could fairly be classed as a neo-Freudian.

It is therefore reasonable to allow that Dr. Bevan-Brown is entitled to write with authority on the subject of Mental Hygiene and the causes of psychological disorders, and it is with interest that we turn to his evaluation of the factors capable of promoting the former or leading to the development of the latter.

Now that man within the last generation has at last turned his attention to the study of man himself, it is clear that much advance in our knowledge of the psychology of health and disease may be expected in the near future. I do not suppose Dr. Bevan-Brown will claim that his conclusions are final; but, based as they are on thirty years' experience, they must command close attention. Indeed, inasmuch as they deal with a subject in which, in the nature of the case, personal experience is the only guide, his conclusions could only be modified or refuted by greater or more extended experience, which, in fact, may be confidently expected to confirm them.

We are all aware of the emotional malaise which to-day affects individuals, nations and indeed mankind. It is apparent that the problem of Mental Hygiene must receive our urgent attention if Western Civilisation is to survive.

ix

Dr. Bevan-Brown makes this clear; but he does more than pose the problem, he indicates the way to its solution. Fear and kindred emotions are at the root of most of mankind's troubles, and if freedom from fear is to be achieved, we must eradicate the sources of fear, and instead drink deep from the well-springs of love in its fullest sense. It should really come as no surprise that this process must start in the first year of life.

W. H. St. John-Brooks

B.A. (Cantab.), M.B., B.Ch. (Cantab.), M.R.C.P. (London)
Physician, Timaru Hospital, N.Z.

INTRODUCTION

THE purpose of this little volume is to draw attention to the need in our day and in our culture for preventive psychiatry, or perhaps more correctly, the understanding and practice of mental hygiene.

In our generation, largely through the work of Sigmund Freud, great advances have been made in the understanding of mental illness, and our knowledge of its origins and sources, and in our capacity to treat it.

Many chronic mental illnesses, especially the psychoneuroses, can now be successfully treated by psychotherapy; but in the more severe cases this process is inordinately costly in time and money as well as labour, and frequently involves considerable distress for the patient. Operations on the body, however well performed, cause some distress to the patient; and psychotherapy of the more radical kind required in the more severe and chronic cases means an operation on the mind, occupying not a few hours, but many months or years. In skilled hands it has proved itself as a very successful means of cure. But on account of the long period of time required for one patient it is a most uneconomical method of dealing with the whole problem of mental illness.

The rational method is to prevent these diseases developing by educating people (especially adolescents) in the principles of mental health, and so eventually to breed a community in which mental disease is the exception rather than the rule as at present.

In our generation this has become a practical possibility. The evidence is now overwhelming that a large proportion of this illness has its origin in the earliest years of life and as a consequence of faulty nurture; and it is at this period especially that the principles of mental health must be applied. It is a matter of good parenthood, and especially good motherhood.

By the ' earliest years of life ' we mean, broadly, the first five years. Since the work of Freud became known it was recognized that the mental health or ill-health of an individual largely depended upon the type of nurture he received during this period. It is only in more recent years that psychiatrists have come to realize that it is the first two years (before the age of language) that are pre-eminent in importance. Latest of all comes the conviction of the supreme importance of the first year. This clearly includes the period of breast feeding, or perhaps we ought to say, *should* include it.

In the opinion of the writer, the experiences of breast-feeding are crucial in determining subsequent mental health; and the burden of the book is concerned with the importance of this period.

Since it is the mother who must do the breast-feeding, the book is largely concerned with motherhood, and seeks to show that much of the trouble in which we now find ourselves is due to inadequate motherhood.

The realization that the first year, or even the first six months are of supreme importance means that what is known as the Oedipus complex, or Oedipus situation in psychopathology has ceased to be central in importance, and must yield pride of place to the earlier experiences of the first mother-child relationship.*

If the breast-feeding relationship has failed, the later Oedipus situation may involve acute problems; and the same applies to bowel training: if the breast-feeding relationship has been satisfactory the Oedipus-complex will not become a problem. It should be understood that knowledge of principles of mental hygiene or prophylaxis has been derived largely from the results of treating sick people, as well as by testing out these principles by applying them (via parents) in the lives of developing children.

It is therefore, I think, worth while to digress briefly into some aspects of analytical psychotherapy.

Because psychotherapy of a radical type (analytical methods) tends to be very protracted and time-consuming, psychiatrists and psychotherapists have continually sought to find some means of shortening the process. This search has not been very successful hitherto. Analytical treatment involves the recovery of experiences belonging to, or characteristic of the earliest years of life, and the full comprehension

* Cf. Drs. I. and J. I. Suttie, *The Mother: Agent or Object*, Parts I and II. British Journ. of Med. Psych., 1932-3.

of these (as feelings and emotional experiences) in consciousness. (Recovery does not mean merely remembering them as factual experiences: in fact, the process is quite different from ordinary memory.) It is a fair provisional assumption, therefore, that the earliest experiences—those associated with the first year—are likely to be the most difficult to recover and the last to emerge. Therefore the earlier in life the crucial experiences are presumed to have occurred, the longer the time the treatment is likely to occupy. (This assumption, though widely held, is not completely correct, and requires qualification; but such excursions would take us rather far from our main theme. For our present purpose we may fairly assume that the provisional assumption is substantially correct.) The physician, then, in a certain proportion of cases, hopes that the patient's problems may be solved (i.e. a cure produced) without reference to, or analysis of the patient's earliest experiences: in this way he hopes to shorten the length of treatment and be ready to begin with the next person on his waiting list who is clamouring for help.

This hope and search also becomes more urgent when for any reason it is impossible for the patient to devote more than a relatively short time for his treatment.

I have shared fully in this common search for methods to abbreviate analytical treatment, and have to confess that, in the main, attempts to shorten the process have tended actually to lengthen it. This also is a common experience of physicians. I am not referring here, of course, to those people for whom a more superficial type of treatment, palliative and non-analytical, is adequate or perhaps the only practicable method.

In the last ten years especially I have had a number of cases in whom I have thought at the outset that their problem was sufficiently superficial to be capable of solution without reference to the earliest experiences. In many such cases I have been greatly impressed by the fact that despite my hope and plan, the patient has led me 'back' (see * below) to first year and breast-feeding experiences (or the deprivation thereof) and compelled me to refer to these experiences as the original source of his problem and therefore as the necessary avenue to its solution. I do not mean, of course, that the patient has consciously or intentionally led me 'back' in this way: he has done this unconsciously, and involuntarily: only later, and with difficulty, does he realize what he has been doing. Incidentally, this is disconcerting to those ill-informed critics and sceptics who suppose that the analyst diligently and systematically imposes upon the patient a preconceived theory as to the nature and origin of his illness.

There are many cases in which it is obvious at the outset that it will be useless to attempt anything but a full investigation and analysis of first year vicissitudes; but these experiences of mine in recent years, in which the patient himself has compelled my attention to first year experiences, when I hoped and thought that this might not be necessary, have been one of the factors impelling me to write these pages.

In other words, as the years go on, it is my patients who compel me ever more and more to realize the vital importance of the earliest mother-child relationship—provided I have enough discernment and willingness to listen; and they tell me in language, expression, gesture, and behaviour which it is impossible to misinterpret.* Earlier in the text I stated that the patient led me ' back ' to first year experiences. This requires some elucidation—it is really a 'façon de parler '— it suggests that the patient has somehow gone back in time and led me back with him. Only in a limited sense is this true. With him, as with most of us, the past and the present are one; in large measure we are the sum and result of ' previous experiences.' The actual fact is that these patients are still living in their first year so far as emotional development and personal relationships are concerned. For the sake of appearances as well as for self-esteem they must heavily disguise this fact from themselves as well as from others so far as possible. One might add that this arrest in the first year is not confined to those (relatively few) who come for treatment but of many more who seek no physician.

It should be emphasized again that they are in this condition not of their own free will or choice, not even consciously, but as a result of experiences when they were helpless to understand or choose, and under the overwhelming compulsions of fear and guilt.

In the foregoing I have used the phrases ' satisfactory mother-child relationship ', ' if the breast-feeding relationship

has failed ', etc. Some elucidation of these phrases is necessary.

The main theme of the book is the importance of breast-
feeding for subsequent mental—and physical—health. But
this statement is insufficient. It is not enough to say that the
baby must be breast-fed in the sense that he must be offered
the breast at specified intervals and thus provided with a
nutrient fluid. It is possible for many women conscientiously
to accept the doctrine of the importance of breast-feeding and
to proceed diligently and dutifully to apply it, and yet to fail
miserably to supply what the child really needs. It is the
form and manner of this breast-feeding process that is of
paramount importance. It is a personal relationship, and not
a bowser-like process.

It is not enough for the mother passively (still less timidly)
to offer the breast for the child to take. An appropriate attitude in the mother is required which could be expressed by
the phrases ' active wooing ', ' invitation ' and ' encouragement'.
The situation would then be that the mother wants to feed
the baby with much the same kind of feeling as the baby
wants to be fed; and that the baby is able to appreciate the
situation.

A typical utterance of a patient during treatment is as
follows: ' Don't want just to be fed: want to belong: want to
feel part of mother—joined on—she seems to want to get the
thing over—as if I'm a nuisance—doesn't seem to like me—
doesn't seem to like these feelings I have—they must be bad.'
These bald words written thus are not very impressive or
convincing. They are shorn of the intense emotional stress
and anxiety with which they are charged. It is not possible
to convey this in the written word.

This need to be wanted, valued, liked, approved as well as
fed, was not discovered by analytical treatment; it is and has
been long known by good mothers. What is learnt from
analysis is its vital importance, and the grievous consequences
that ensue from its frustration. This matter is discussed at
greater length in the text.

We understand that the ' Cornelian Corner ' have coined a
phrase ' self-demand ' feeding. This we interpret to mean that
the child shall be given the breast whenever he wants or needs

it. We strongly support such a practice. Here the mother responds to the child's approach just as in 'active wooing' the child responds. They together make a mutual reciprocal relationship characteristic of any intimate personal relationship.

There is a report on the 'Advisability of Breast Feeding' by the U.S. National Research Council which seems to me to be a balanced and reasonable summary. In it Dr. Aldrich states that there is a great need of concrete proof of the value of breast-feeding from the psychological angle. This word 'proof' is a difficult one in any scientific field: it is specially difficult in the psychological field. I therefore wonder what kind of proof would be acceptable to the people Dr. Alrich has in mind. It seems to me that the only 'proof' available would be the results in the adult personality of those who had been satisfactorily breast-fed and those who had not. One would therefore have to wait twenty or twenty-five years for the proof. and even then the logicians and methodologists would object to the word being so applied. Great difficulty would also arise in that it would be of no value to record results merely on the reported fact that a certain child had been breast-fed. It is fallacious to speak of breast-feeding as if it had always the same significance as a human experience.

To be 'adequate' or 'satisfactory' for the child's nurture and subsequent emotional development it should be a total relationship between two persons (mother and baby) with both physical and emotional components and involving complete harmony in both components. It will be a difficult matter to investigate this statistically. We here have no shadow of doubt of the importance of breast-feeding as provided by a healthy and emotionally-mature mother. The evidence of this in both mother and babies is overwhelming. quite apart from the impressive results derived from the treatment of persons who have been deprived of it. But I doubt whether we could offer a proof of our conviction which would satisfy the logicians. Unfortunately the vast majority of physicians at present are not equipped to recognize 'satisfactory' breast-feeding when they see it, nor to assess the results of it in personality development. The people so qualified are as yet few in any country.

THE SOURCES OF LOVE AND FEAR

1.—PIONEERING

PHILOSOPHY, it is said, begins with wonder. The essence of science is the asking of questions. One of the things that distinguishes a man from a cow is that, so far as we know, a cow does not ask questions. It is unfortunately true that a large number of men also do not ask questions; but of course there are other qualities besides the asking of questions, fortunately for them, which distinguish men from cows. Nevertheless, the asking of questions is a very important part of human activity, and progress very largely depends upon it. To state that if one never asks a question, one will never get an answer, is clearly a truism, but it is a truism worth stating and emphasizing. If we ask questions, we may get an answer; the answer may not come immediately but after a long interval of search. If we do not ask questions, we never get an answer. Sometimes if we ask questions, we are rewarded by an answer which is much richer in information than we expected when we asked it. So it is with Sigmund Freud of Vienna. He, a physician, was not satisfied with the conventional and orthodox opinions of his contemporaries with regard to the nature and origin of those disorders of the mind which we now call neuroses or psycho-neuroses. Being that particular type of personality, he felt he must find out the truth about these things, and he proceeded therefore to ask his patients questions about themselves. In the first instance his questions were usually introduced by the words 'When?' 'How?' and 'Why?' He was not attempting to treat them or cure them at first, but merely to discover how and why they became ill.

This procedure required infinite patience; and this was a quality which Freud possessed and used in the pursuit of his aim. He was both rewarded and astonished at the results of his own questioning. As he proceeded with his task he found with some at least of his patients, that his questions need not be repeated as frequently, but that the patient's answer became more and more complete and illuminating. Eventually his questions were reduced to a minimum and consisted in merely asking the patient to relax his mind and body, to avoid any selection in his thoughts and just to go on reporting what came into his mind, whatever the material might be. The result was his discovery that all these illnesses could be traced to sources in the patient's childhood, and moreover to the earlier childhood years.

This fact that he discovered in repeated experiments of this type was previously unknown to himself, to other physicians and to the patient. One of the remarkable features about it was that the experiences in childhood which were sources of neuroses in adult life had not been previously in the patient's memory; in fact, were entirely forgotten; and thus all connection between them and the subsequent illness had been lost. Thus was born the theory and doctrine known as Psychoanalysis. But now Freud made another remarkable discovery which he had not anticipated. He found that many of these patients who had submitted to this long investigation and enquiry were either cured of their troubles or very much relieved; so that what began as a method of investigation turned out to be at the same time an effective method of treatment. This was the beginning of that form of psychotherapy or psychological treatment known as Psycho-analysis. The word Psycho-analysis thus has two denotations. It is the name for a system of theories of psychopathology and also a name for a method of treatment of mental disorders. It should be understood that the success of the treatment depended *not* merely on the physician eliciting information from the patient, but on the patient's discovery of feelings and experiences in himself.

As time went on Freud collected around him a group of followers who became very enthusiastic, and who discovered that if they approached the task in the same spirit as Freud had done, they were able to produce the same results both as regards investigation and as regards cure. Also, with a large body of workers, psycho-analytical theory gradually became more refined and more elaborated; until at length it was found that the origins of these troubles went back not only to early childhood but to infancy and even to the first weeks of life. In other words, if a method could be found of answering completely these questions why, how and when the

2

patient's illness first began, and if the patient himself could answer these questions with complete conviction, he was then cured.

Now it will be clear that if we are able to obtain a clear answer to these questions ' why ', ' how ' and ' when '; and if we then find that the answer to the ' when ' is always in early childhood and to the ' how ' and ' why ' because of some feature in the handling of the child by the parents or others, we can also proceed to infer, that if the behaviour or character of the parents involved had been different, the person would not have got ill.

This is the third great discovery arising out of Freud's investigation, and is surely the most important of the three; though Freud never expected such a result when he asked his original questions. Moreover, Freud himself did not stress the importance for mental hygiene of this deduction from his findings. It is, however, the most important of the three because it means the development of a system of mental prophylaxis. In other words, we can now learn what parents must do and be if their children are to grow up with healthy minds. Such theories of prophylaxis, however, arising in such a way, were not likely to meet with wide acceptance until enough time had elapsed for them to be tested in practice. It is only very recently that we can say that enough time has elapsed to permit of such testing and it is found that, when put to the test, the system works.

2.—PSYCHOTHERAPY

EARLIER it was stated that Freud's associates, in order to obtain his results in treatment, had to work with the same spirit as Freud himself had done. This needs further explanation. It is not necessary here to explain in detail the technique of the treatment called Psycho-analysis, but certain features of it are very important for our present purpose. It was found that neither the investigation nor the treatment were successful unless the physician adopted and maintained a certain attitude to the patient. The essential features of this attitude were a genuine sympathy, a quiet and unobtrusive friendliness, the total absence of criticism, superiority, moralizing or argument, and the presence of a high degree of patience and tolerance. It was soon found that in order that a physician might be able to achieve and maintain such an attitude to a patient over a long period of time, a careful training was necessary. This training occupied a long period of time; because this is an attitude to people which is very different indeed from the attitude which people usually adopt in their personal relationship with one another, and also different from the attitude adopted by many parents toward their children. This latter frequently involves a high degree of impatience, irritability, superiority, moral criticism, intolerance or even hostility.

Now another interesting question arose; what was the significance of this peculiar and rather unusual attitude that it was necessary for the physician to adopt toward his patient? It was certainly necessary in order to produce a cure; but was it merely a convenient and clever device for attaining this end, with no further purpose or usefulness? Reflection upon this question led to the remarkable conclusion that this attitude corresponded in all essential respects to the attitude of parents whose children grew up mentally healthy. This, then, surely is an epoch-making discovery. This it is that makes Freud one of those figures whose arrival marks the beginning of a new era, in the same category as Darwin, Newton, and Copernicus. The discovery clearly shows that in essence the method of treatment known as psycho-analysis cures the patient by providing him with a new and more adequate parent with whom, as it were, he can live his childhood over again, or perhaps, if you will, through whom he can be born again. Like a good parent, the psycho-analyst has to *be* something to his patient rather than *do* something to him.

3.—INCIDENCE OF NEUROSIS

THE Anglo-Saxons and most Europeans are heavily permeated with neurosis. In approximately 10 per cent. of the population the neurosis is severe enough to cause some obvious disability: in a larger number it is less severe, but still leads to impairment of well-being and social adaptability. This therefore represents a serious social problem which must be attacked sooner or later.

4

These figures will be surprising to many people: there are several reasons why the condition of neurosis is less obvious than the figures indicate. One reason is that many people who suffer from neurosis make great efforts to conceal it, even though the neurosis be severe. Another is that many people who suffer from neurosis are unaware of the fact. A third reason is that neuroses, although they are disorders of the mind, do not always manifest themselves in mental symptoms, but only in physical symptoms and are therefore mistaken for bodily disease.

In view of this one might suppose that the discoveries of Freud, especially those relating to mental hygiene or prophylaxis, would be widely welcomed and accepted. Actually, however, the situation at present is the reverse of this. His discoveries, both in relation to the cause of neurosis, the treatment of it, and more particularly, the resulting principles of mental hygiene have been opposed, attacked and repudiated by the majority of people.

There are several reasons for this. For example, the majority of people resent the idea that they have an unconscious part of their mind which has a potent influence upon their conduct and feelings, i.e. the suggestion that their conduct and feelings are largely determined by factors in themselves of which they are unaware. It seems to be an attack upon their self-esteem, and also tends to produce a feeling of insecurity. Parents also tend to resent the suggestion that neurotic disorders in their children are the result of failures in their own method of handling and nurture. Again, some of the principles of mental hygiene which we shall later discuss are strongly inconsistent with many of the conventional methods of child nurture and training practised by Western civilization: such traditions and conventions, being handed on from generation to generation, are very firmly entrenched and resistant to criticism and modification. All these reasons for hostility and repudiation will be seen to have psychological interest. The intensity with which they are held by large numbers of people is one of the evidences of the truth of the principles so repudiated. A man is liable to become angry if he is told something which he feels is true but which he does not want to accept. Clearly the important question is not whether the vast number of people reject them or not, but whether they are true. This question (whether they are true or not) can only be tested in living; and enough years have passed to demonstrate to people who approach the question free from bias, that the principles when applied in life and in the nurture of children prove to be true.

Other Troubles

In addition to these disorders which are technically described as neuroses, we must add a number of other troubles which afflict society and which also are due to faulty nurture. We must include here conjugal troubles and maladjustments, frigidity, impotence, some sterility, much delinquency; also many of the problems of childhood such as truancy, tempers, tantrums, bedwetting; also the sexual perversions including homosexuality; also stammering, alcoholism and other drug addictions, and much chronic bodily illness—a formidable list. Another indication of the magnitude of the problem can be obtained by examining figures of the U.S. Army rejects on psychiatric grounds, and the proportional number of psychiatric casualties out of the total.

If all these things are due to faulty nurture, and if a large proportion of them can be prevented by healthy nurture, it is urgently necessary to educate as many people as will listen regarding the importance of this matter.

4.—THE IMPORTANCE OF MENTAL HYGIENE

THE attempt to solve the problem of neurosis and mental illness by psychotherapy alone is hopeless—the number of people requiring such treatment is so enormous that an army of therapists would be required. As already mentioned, 10 per cent. of Anglo-Saxons suffer from neurosis.

Looked at from another angle, at least 30 per cent. of all illnesses that are treated by doctors and hospitals is psychic in origin, and should be treated by psychotherapy, whether the symptoms be physical or mental. The Surgeon-General, in a war-time survey, reported that 50 per cent. of hospital beds in U.S.A. were occupied by patients with mental illness and that 90 per cent. had a background of emotional maladjustment.

5.—MENTAL AND PHYSICAL SYMPTOMS

SINCE we have been concerned with those disorders of the mind or personality technically called neuroses, many people tend to assume that these disorders are always manifested by mental or so-called 'nervous' symptoms. (Symptoms are what the patient complains of: signs are what the physician observes or may observe if he looks.) This assumption would be false. In many cases of mental illness the symptoms are largely or wholly physical or bodily; and hosts of people who at present attend doctors and hospitals complaining of bodily symptoms alone are in fact suffering from mental disease and have no bodily disease at all: yet unfortunately many of them are treated by physical and chemical methods as if they had bodily disease. But a disorder which begins as mental or emotional may lead to actual bodily disease; an emotional disorder long continued may in the end produce morbid bodily changes and 'organic' disease which can be observed by medical examination. Examples of this are gastric and duodenal ulcer, colitis and asthma. The correct treatment of these should have been psychic, years before the organic condition developed; but in the absence of such treatment at the appropriate time the resulting organic disease when it eventually develops may be urgent enough to require surgical treatment. Better even than psychic treatment would have been to prevent the original emotional disorders developing by healthy nurture in infancy.

6.—PSYCHO-SOMATIC DISORDERS

IN recent years the term Psycho-somatic Disorders has been introduced: (the word 'psycho-somatic' is Greek for body-mind). It now refers to a group of illnesses in which there are bodily symptoms and recognizable signs of bodily (organic) disease. But in addition to the organic disease the discerning physician will find a long history of emotional disorder which is the real and original cause of the physical disease. Now, since man is (apparently, at least) a mind-body complex, all diseases whatsoever must be in some sense psycho-somatic: but the term is convenient in our present transitional stage to indicate a group of diseases having organic manifestations and an emotional mental cause, which were previously supposed to be due to physical causes only. It is significant that an ever-widening number of disorders is coming to be included in the psycho-somatic group.

The astonishing fact is that the evidence is now overwhelming to show that all this maladjustment has its sources in early nurture. Many psychiatrists engaged in the work of analytical psychotherapy are distressed by the realization that while they are treating, and successfully treating, a few of this great number, they are not reducing the total problem; because thousands more are being produced every day for someone to treat at a later date. Psychotherapy, in regard to the number it can cope with, is very effective as a form of treatment; 70 per cent. or more of all cases treated are greatly benefited. Such treatment involves a most uneconomical expenditure of time, an average (say) of a hundred hours a patient. The only real solution, therefore, is that of mental hygiene and prophylaxis.

7.—HEREDITARY FACTORS

IT will be contended that so far no reference has been made to hereditary factors, and the question will be raised as to whether they do not play an important part in causation. Hereditary factors are important, but never by themselves cause neurosis. They may, of course, be an important factor in such conditions as mental defect and some forms of psychosis. Their importance in the production of neurosis lies in the fact that persons are not all born equal in temperament or basic endowment. For our present purpose, we can say that people are born with great variation in sensitivity. Those who are more sensitive are much more liable to develop neurosis if they experience inadequate nurture than the others whom we may call tougher; on the other hand, if the sensitive ones escape neurosis as a result of satisfactory nurture, they may on account of their extra sensitivity distinguish themselves by some unusual contribution to the community. We are concerned here to be practical: we cannot do anything about heredity: we cannot even diagnose a sensitive child at

8

birth and it is dangerous to guess; but we can do something about nurture.

8.—SCIENCE AND CULTURE

EARLIER it was suggested that the principles of mental hygiene which arise out of Freud's discoveries. were epoch-making in significance. This requires further emphasis. It has been pointed out, and by no one more clearly than John Macmurray, that in the matter of knowing how to live a human life, in the matter of culture, in the matter of living together in communities and nations, men have advanced very little in the last thousand years. We have made enormous strides in the understanding and control of natural forces. and in the physical sciences, but in the matter of understanding ourselves and how to get on with other people we have hardly advanced at all. This situation, as has been pointed out by many people, is responsible for much of the troubles that exist now in the world. If we can now learn how to breed races that are mentally healthy and emotionally mature. composed of beings human in the full sense. the outlook for the world should change profoundly. We are justified then in considering the work of Freud as marking the beginning of a new era; for out of his discoveries there arises at least a possibility and an opportunity for breeding such a race. in which man, having largely mastered physical forces, now begins to study himself and endeavours to comprehend his true nature and the nature of his fellows, and thus master himself. It cannot be maintained that he is master of himself at present.

9.—MENTAL HEALTH AND NURTURE

WE must now return to our central theme and indicate that if any progress is to be made in this direction it will depend upon concentrating on the earlier years of life, on mother-hood and its privileges and responsibilities. and on the mother-infant relationship. For a generation psychiatrists have been so preoccupied with the task of treating and curing the numbers of people applying to them that they have had little time to publish the results of their work and its significance for mental hygiene. In the writer's opinion, it is urgently necessary that this should now be done by as many workers as possible; and this is the essential purpose of this book.

The first thing that the psychiatrist has to make known is that if he seeks to bring about a radical cure of these patients, he has to investigate with the patient crucial experiences of the earliest years of the patient's life. The earliest years are obviously the years 1 to 3. It is within these three years that most of the experiences occur which are the source of an illness appearing ten, twenty or thirty years later. Furthermore, as a result of this work the evidence is continually increasing to show that the first year, and especially what should be the breast-feeding period, is the most important of all.

To the ordinary person who has never investigated the matter and has various common assumptions about the nature of these disorders, these facts seem startling and even incredible. But suppose he is reasonable enough to keep an open mind about the matter and then reflects upon it. It is obvious that a child's mother is, or should be, the first person in the world with whom he associates. She represents the first *personal* relationship, the first *social* relationship, the first *sensuous* relationship, the first *love* relationship. Without any technical knowledge of the subject, it would be reasonable to assume that this relationship, being the first, sets the pattern of all subsequent relationships. That is, of course, supposing he is prepared to grant that the baby in the first year has primitive means of awareness of the existence of another person and is not merely an animated lump of protoplasm! Whether inferred or not, it is this principle that the psychiatrist finds to be true by cumulative evidence, derived from the emotional history of his patients. The word ' history ' here must not be misunderstood. The patients themselves have of course no memory of these early years, and if they are told at the beginning of their treatment that the sources of their troubles lie in these years, they tend to be as incredulous as anyone else. A long and arduous investigation into matters previously unconscious is necessary. At the end of a successful treatment, however, they have a feeling of conviction about the importance of their earlier experiences which is most interesting to observe. It is an inner conviction based on living experiences. and even the physician. supposing he wished to do so, would not be able to shake it. We have used this word ' experiences ' frequently and the reader may be impatient to learn what kind of experience is implied here which is so fateful for later life. *All the experiences involve situations in which the child was ignored, rejected, undervalued, disapproved of, scolded, punished, frustrated, discouraged, intimidated or frightened by the mother*, or perhaps by some other person who is taking the place of the mother and frequently should not be doing so.

Having indicated the conditions which tend towards neurosis, we must now consider the opposite question. namely what are the conditions tending towards health? They can be summed up in one short sentence: ' The child must be loved. and especially by the mother'. To many this will seem a platitude: many also will say that the vast majority of mothers do love their children. Now investigation shows that not all mothers do in fact love their children in the sense that is required; though they may be firmly convinced that they do. It can be shown that it is only a minority of mothers who do love their children in the sense that is required. They are not necessarily to blame for this: many of them with the best will in the world are not capable of such an attitude without expert help. As regards the question of platitude—to say ' The child must be loved ' is easy. but to explain what this means is less easy. We must embark upon this task. ' Loving ' includes ' liking '. ' valuing '. ' respecting '. ' protecting'. ' enjoying '. and transcends all these.

It may fairly be assumed that in humans. as well as in many animals. love of parent (especially mother) for offspring is naturally based upon instinct; in other words we may legitimately talk of ' maternal instinct'. If it is true that many humans do not love their offspring adequately. then they must be disabled in some way: there must be forces at work interfering with the free operation of this instinct. It would be foolish and futile to announce such an apparent platitude as ' The child must be loved ' without indicating some of the factors or forces interfering with the development and operation of maternal love.

First then it is the *child* that must be loved, objectively, that is to say, as he is, both physically and mentally, without reserve, without ' ifs ' and 'buts'. And this applies from the first hour—even minutes—of extra-uterine life. If so then it is clearly necessary to know what kind of creature a baby is. For on this matter various rather arbitrary opinions have been held. By some he has been regarded as an angel direct from heaven (i.e. not human) : by others as liable to become a little devil unless precautions in the form of ' discipline ' are taken; by others still, a lump of animated protoplasm with no particular feelings except an appetite. Some, on the basis of a quasi-religious outlook, regard him as a fallen creature, or as having been born in sin, and therefore actually or potentially bad or sinful. If the mother holds any of these views as to the nature of the child, her relationship with him is liable to be disastrous. For example, if she regards him as potentially bad, it will be impossible for her to love him adequately in the sense in which we are using that word, for then she must needs alter, correct or ' improve ' him. We shall refer to the effects of this policy later; but the first is of course that the child feels unloved but is quite incapable of understanding why.

It is perhaps important to mention here another common and insidious fallacy. The child during the first decade or even up to puberty is not a miniature adult and to assume that he is this is both unjust and dangerous. He is no more a miniature adult than a cotyledon is a miniature tree. This difficulty, however, usually arises with children from two years and upwards, and not in infancy.

The Baby is a Person

What then is the nature of the infant? At birth he closely resembles the offspring of the higher mammals. He differs from these in two respects (1) his extreme helplessness and (2) in his potentiality—what he may become if he is well nurtured. *He is an embryo,* a going concern, a dynamic organism, a person, and a potential personality. He is a bundle of forces, psychic in nature, which are as yet primitive, autonomous, unintegrated, unco-ordinated and uncontrolled. There is as yet no ' I,' or ego, or personality to organize or control them. He has emerged into a noisy world from an

12

intra-uterine situation where he was in complete equilibrium; and he needs the greatest care to help him through this violent and relatively sudden change.

First Need—Security

He is very prone to fear. This proneness of the infant to fear is of the utmost importance in early life. It must be constantly watched for, and he must be protected against it. To be exposed to fear is unquestionably the greatest psychic danger of the child in the first year. In the second year when he can to some extent fend for himself, the danger is less, though still present. It is remarkable and perhaps significant of the immaturity of our culture that so many people, even so many mothers, fail to realize the proneness of the infant to fear, and even tend to doubt the fact when it is pointed out. I have actually seen it stated in a standard text-book of academic psychology that a young infant does not experience much fear! Such adults will naïvely suppose that because they apprehend no danger and see no reason for fear that therefore the child should feel just as they do; and that, as there is in fact no danger from the adult point of view, it is stupid for him to fear and irritating if he cries. At this point I should like to refer to a little book, *Baby's Point of View*, by Joyce Partridge, an English surgeon and psychiatrist, published by Oxford Medical Publications. This little book is the most valuable I know regarding infant welfare and the author is admirably qualified as an authority. She gives a set of rules, one of which is ' Never leave a baby (in the first year) alone to cry.' This is an absolute rule: it does not say ' pick the baby up every time he cries ' nor does it forbid this if necessary: but it does say that while crying he must not be left alone. He may be crying because he is hungry, cold, too hot, wet, etc.; if so, these things may be attended to. But he may be none of these things: he may be crying because he is frightened, and if not reassured early this is a dangerous condition. It should be realized that the young baby is the most helpless creature in organic nature; he is utterly depen- dent, and he needs not only food, oxygen and water but also human association. The realization that his mother is there (when awake) or will always come if he needs her gives him a feeling of security, protection and confidence. Thus under

13

these conditions he may never fall into fear at all. In the absence of such protection he certainly will do so; and the fear he then experiences is much more devastating than the type of fear the adult normally experiences: it is all-pervading panic—because he is quite unable to understand the situation, to fight it, or to run away: he can only wait for someone else to deal with it. Thus the first need of the infant is *security* which he derives from constant association with his mother. If the mother realizes this need and meets it in the earliest weeks, the child acquires a feeling of security and confidence in the mother which will enable him to meet emergencies without undue disturbance. If it is not met he will become an anxious child and may continue for months to cry immediately he is left. There has recently existed a school of infant nurture which has held the view that it is good to let the baby cry and leave him alone, that, since there is no (adult) danger, he must learn that it is stupid to cry. They suggest that this is the way to teach him self-reliance, and even that it is wrong to go to him when he cries because he is doing it on purpose to annoy or dominate his environment! This doctrine is not only very foolish but also pernicious and dangerous. Psychiatrists can all produce cases to show that it has laid the foundation for a permanent anxiety state in later life. Those who are familiar with the characteristics of an anxiety state will realize that it has all the characteristics of the panic of the infant: it is irrational, it is about everything or nothing in particular, it can neither be fought nor escaped from. it is all-pervading. The baby must not be left alone to cry. This. then, is the first principle of child nurture which we learn from the treatment of people suffering from emotional disorders; and if an infant in the early weeks and months of life is allowed to remain frightened and alone, this experience may be the origin of an anxiety state which may persist into adult life. There is nothing especially surprising about such a statement; the child's first impressions of the world into which he has come are that it is inhospitable, dangerous and lonely. .and it is no use seeking help. He must try to fend for himself and not expect help; but he cannot fend for himself, he is helpless. It is not a matter for surprise that such impressions may colour his view of the world and the people in it permanently. Much of his subsequent conduct will be devoted

14

to the object of making himself as secure as he can in an insecure world. (Incidentally it will follow that if there is a large proportion of such individuals in a nation they will tend to assume that other nations have hostile intentions towards them, and will concentrate on national security as well as personal security.) But there is a further reason why these early impressions become permanent attitudes. The child, being unable to reason or compare, does not proceed to consider that his mother is not perhaps as competent a person as she might be, and therefore not an adequate mother in that she does not comfort him; but he early begins to feel (not think) that the reason for this neglect is that he himself is valueless, worthless, insignificant, possibly bad in some way; therefore, in order to be loved and valued he will have to alter himself in some way or another. Here is the beginning of emotional conflict and repression; and the feelings of anxiety become involved with feelings of inferiority and guilt. If these dangers are to be avoided, the infant must be in close association with the mother for the first hours, days, weeks of life, so that whenever he wakes he has the feeling that she is near. Such an association makes the closest possible approximation to his intra-uterine security and placental attachment, which has just been broken. If this transition period is managed in this way for the first month or six weeks, the infant will acquire confidence in his environment and will soon be willing to lie awake alone in his cot without fear. We could well learn some lessons in motherhood from the behaviour of some of the higher mammals. We are inclined to consider that we are much superior as human beings to the higher mammals, but observation will show that some human mothers are inferior, as mothers, to the higher mammals.

Operations

While on the subject of security, we must refer to operations.

However skilfully managed, these are liable to be terrifying experiences to the child. The special danger is that usually the child is separated from his mother. Analytical treatment frequently reveals the feeling that she has wilfully or callously deserted him in his greatest need. From the point of view of prophylaxis it is important to avoid all operations except to

15

save life before the age of four or five. The danger is less after this age, when the situation can be explained to the child. If an operation must be done it is important that the child be not separated from his mother.

Circumcision

It is extraordinary that in our day this rather barbaric rite should be practised almost as a routine with infants. From the psychological point of view it is dangerous with or without an anaesthetic. In the rare case where a child cannot urinate it may be done, but it is otherwise unjustifiable. Apparently the practice is based on a morbid fear of masturbation, and is unconsciously propitiatory. When performed at the age of two or three it is frequently the basis of severe castration fears.

Second Need—Sensuousness

We must now consider the second great need of the infant. But when we say ' second ' we do not mean secondary in importance. In the first place we will call this need *nutrition*. This word usually refers to a physiological need, but we hope to indicate that this is only a part of the nutritive need of the child. There are systems of infant welfare which start from the assumption that if a baby receives a certain proportion of protein, fat, carbohydrate and minerals, water and vitamins, at regular intervals, if he is kept warm and has napkins changed periodically then all will be well with him.

This assumption means that he in all respects resembles an engine or a piece of mechanism, or is in no respect different from a calf or lamb. If this assumption were correct it would be sound policy, as is so often recommended, to provide these substances through a bottle or a tube, thus avoiding what is regarded as the exacting task of breast-feeding. It is the duty of the psychiatrist to point out that this doctrine is false and that it is responsible for a host of troubles which continue into adult life, but which are never connected with their actual source. *The baby at birth is a person* and not a machine, and, being a person, has a need for close association with another person. And this person must have certain feelings and attitudes towards him, of which we shall have more to say presently. At the moment we will mention only

16

that this person must be conscious and sentient. Before attempting to explain this matter further, we must draw attention to a principle which is important both biologically and psychologically and which underlies the whole matter.

We belong to a race of organisms which is the result of a long process of evolution. In common with all our ancestors, both mammalian and pre-mammalian, we are endowed with a very strong instinct tending towards intimate association with another individual. We can call this instinct or tendency a copulative tendency. Unfortunately the word 'copulation' has been limited to the mechanical aspect of the reproductive act. The term has a much wider application than this and we are using it in that larger sense. This copulative tendency is to be observed in creatures as far back as the protozoa and it is true that in the more primitive organism it usually subserves reproduction. In the mammals and in man this copulative tendency is of supreme importance in the first months of life. We are here seeking to point out that the infant has an urgent need to copulate with a person, to wit, the mother, through the medium of the nipple and the mouth; and this need transcends the mere need for chemical sustenance. Clearly here this copulative process still subserves reproduction in that it has to do with the nurture of the infant, but it is a function of organs that are not commonly regarded as genital or reproductive. If we now pass from biological language to psychological language, and speak in human terms, we could say baldly that the infant requires love as well as milk. What the psychiatrist has discovered by a generation of labour is that even though the infant be provided with all the chemical substances necessary, at regular intervals in correct quantity, he may not thrive: he may thrive physically to a degree, while as a *personality* he may fail to thrive: but he may even in these circumstances fail to thrive physically. We are evidently drawn to the conclusion that if a child is to thrive mentally and physically he needs to be breast-fed, and this proposition can be made with confidence: *There are risks attaching to the development of any baby that has the misfortune not to be breast-fed.*

Quality of Breast-feeding

But even this conclusion needs further elaboration. Even

though the baby may be breast-fed in the mechanical sense, and obtain milk from his mother of the correct chemical quality and quantity, he may still not thrive. Thus we come to the crux of the matter and the truth we hope to convey: unless this breast-feeding process is a true human copulation, that is to say, unless it is a mutual reciprocal and personal act as well as a mechanical process, the baby may not thrive. Again, it may be more explicitly stated that the breast-feeding must not be only chemical and physical but a *love relationship* if the baby is to thrive.

We must endeavour to explain what a love relationship is. The essential requirement here is that the mother enjoy this breast-feeding association and enjoy the baby in it, and also that the baby know that the mother is so enjoying it and him. It will at once be asked how possibly could a baby of one month old have any such knowledge or perception. I do not think I can give a convincing proof that the baby arrives at this perception; but I know that he has this ability; and this can be confirmed from the evidence of that select body of mothers who have fully performed the breast-feeding function. The evidence that I have from patients who are reproducing these experiences in the course of treatment of emotional disorders indicates that the sensuous experiences of the baby at the breast include the following components:—

(1) Intense sensations derived from contact of lips, tongue and palate with the nipple.

(2) Sensations from contact of nose and cheek with the breast.

(3) General sensations of softness and warmth.

(4) Sensations of being enfolded, supported and held or embraced.

(5) Bodily odours from the mother.

(6) Sensations of satisfaction in mouth, pharynx, oesophagus and stomach of receiving warm milk.

(7) Sounds of appropriate quality made by the mother.

(8) Sensations in the hands of caressing, squeezing and patting the breast.

(9) (not in the earlier weeks). Sight impressions of the mother's facial expression.

18

As regards (1) it should be noted that a young baby is 'all mouth'; his mouth is paramount and his whole being is centred and focussed in it, the muscles surrounding the mouth being already strong and well-adapted for activity. It is to be expected, then, that the physical condition of the nipple during the process of breast-feeding is of vital importance—its size, its tension, its firmness, its elasticity, its vitality, its smoothness and response to the stimulus of sucking. It is very illuminating to learn from adult patients vivid details of such impressions; though as a rule these are the conditions of the nipple they are yearning for but not experiencing. It is necessary to add that many of these patients are adult males who know (intellectually) nothing about the matter and have had (since infancy) no such experience. These complaints (given under great stress) are of smallness (they cannot get hold of it), dryness, roughness, lifelessness, flaccidity, lack of response, etc. Sometimes they have a great feeling of frustration which they attribute to not being allowed to fondle the breast with their hands (their hands and arms being presumably wrapped up).

Another distressing feeling commonly reported is one of anxiety—there is an impression that they must hurry, the mother is rather impatient because she is busy and has other things to do and therefore must get this business over: therefore there is the feeling that the breast may be taken away before the child is satisfied. The point is that he never will be satisfied under these conditions: he wants and needs a love response from the mother and will go on sucking more and more frantically in the hope of getting it. This may lead to vomiting and distress, etc., etc.

Returning then to the problem—how does the baby know that his mother is enjoying the breast-feeding situation and him in it (or not) and is therefore in fact loving him? My own conviction about this is that it is chiefly through the medium of component (1) (see above) i.e. from his perception of the condition and response of the nipple through sensations in lips, tongue, palate and pharynx.

For further consideration of this see later section.

10.—LOVE AND DUTY

WE live in a culture in which duty is regarded as a very high ideal. A mother may say that she regards it as her highest duty to breast-feed her child, but cannot by any means bring herself to really enjoy the process, and hence her breast-feeding is a sacrifice of herself. This would seem a very high and essentially human motive. But unfortunately such a motive is inadequate here. The astonishing fact is that the baby has the means of knowing that the mother is feeding him merely from a sense of duty, and he will feel unwanted, unloved, and experience consequent reactions of depression, fear, rage, etc. The inevitable conclusion is that in the nurture of the young at least, duty as a motive is inferior to love, and love involves not sacrifice of oneself to another person but *enjoyment of that person.*

We mentioned that fear is one of the reactions likely to occur in the situation we have described; that is, where the mother feeds the baby from a sense of duty and not enjoyment. Clearly this links up with the primary need that we discussed earlier, that of security. In fact, the need for security is intimately connected with this need for sensuous love which we have indicated. The two are inseparable in actual experience though it is convenient to consider them separately for purposes of description.

We have introduced a word here, ' *sensuous* ' which we used earlier and without explanation.

Freud and his followers have used the word ' sexual ' in this connection, viz., to refer to that type of feeling experienced by both the mother and the infant in this copulative breast-feeding process. We think that the use of this word ' sexual ' has led to confusion, and much prefer the word ' sensuous.' Some people, particularly mothers, describe this as ' physical ' enjoyment.

This leads us to draw attention to another principle, viz., that all healthy, vital and biological functions are attended by sensuousness or, if you like, pleasure or enjoyment. Such processes are eating, drinking, micturition, defaecation, breast-feeding, parturition, coitus, bathing, singing, dancing, muscular activity.

It is evident, then, that this sensuousness or enjoyment

20

which should be experienced by both parties in the breast-feeding situation subserves *nutrition*: that which accompanies coitus, and which may more appropriately be called sexual, subserves *reproduction*. From the point of view of mental hygiene, which is our concern, the essential conclusion is that the subsequent physical and mental health of any individual depends very largely on whether or not he has experienced a true biological and psychological relationship with his mother in the first months of life, i.e. on whether he has been loved as an infant by his mother in a completely human sense.

We referred earlier to calves and lambs, as if what would do for them would not do for human beings, but it is interesting to note that recently attention has been drawn to the fact that the principle applies to these animals also. We are not so much concerned with the social behaviour of calves and lambs, but I understand that authorities maintain that physical differences can be detected between calves that have been breast-fed and those fed from a bucket.—(Mary King, *Truby King, The Man*, p. 171 [Allen and Unwin].)

11.—INSTINCT v. PSEUDO-SCIENCE

THERE are two conspicuous features of our culture:

(1) A tendency to undervalue instinctive feeling and emotion in favour of a vaunted ' science.'

(2) The alarming extent of disability and illness arising from emotional maladjustment.

These two features can be related to one another. For example, it is well known that a mother's hearing apparatus is sensitively attuned to a baby's cry; that she has a strong impulse to go to and comfort the baby when it cries—that is, of course, if it is within earshot. In many obstetrical institutions this situation is met by removing the baby so far from the mother that its cries cannot be heard by her, and even by teaching the mother that it is foolish to keep on responding to this cry because in their view the baby has been fed adequately and is physically comfortable and has no need to cry. The latter teaching is based on a pseudo-science which sets an altogether disproportionate value on system and asepsis.

Similarly, women who are emotionally mature wish to be conscious throughout the whole function of parturition and have a feeling that this is right for them, but it is difficult for them to resist the strong propaganda in favour of using the apparatus of modern science, including anaesthetics and instruments.

(We have used the phrase 'emotionally mature' without explaining it. We shall return to this matter later.)

This repudiation of instinct and instinctive feeling is associated with an attempt to deny our connection with other organisms and our animal ancestry, and has had serious consequences. It is not necessary for humans to regard themselves as in all respects equivalent to animals and therefore unable to attain a higher measure of development, but it is necessary to value and accept our animal inheritance and build upon it. A friend of mine reported the other day that a friend of hers had been advised by an American physician as follows: 'Do not bother about breast-feeding your baby. It isn't worth the trouble. He will do just as well on the bottle.' On what kind of evidence does this physician base his statement? In order to test the truth of it he will have to examine the physical and mental health and capacity for social adjustment of this baby twenty-five or more years later. We must, however, consider cases where breast-feeding appears to fail even though the milk supply is adequate and the baby improves when put on the bottle. This may occur, and there are reasons for it. If a mother is so unadapted to maternity as to be unable to enter into a personal relationship with her baby in the process of breast-feeding and manifests feelings of timidity, shrinking, apprehension, disgust and so on, i.e. if the mother is 'frigid' as regards the baby, the baby may become so disturbed as to be unable to play his part. In such a situation bottle feeding, though a *pis aller*, may be preferable.

This partly answers the question: 'Is it always a disaster for a baby to be taken off the breast and put on a bottle?' The first answer to this is that for the welfare of the baby nothing can replace *adequate* breast-feeding; but if this is impossible, then the bottle may have to be resorted to, and may even be preferable in such cases as that mentioned above. But if the child is given the bottle, it is vitally important that the process imitate that of breast-feeding as closely as possible, i.e. the way in which the baby is held, and the actual manner in which the bottle is given. It is one thing to hold the baby close to the breast in the breast-feeding position, and give the baby the bottle when it is certain that he wants it, and quite another thing to poke the bottle at him while he is lying independently in a cot or bed; or to hold the baby in a vice-like grip, and force the teat into his mouth. Many people who cheerfully advocate bottle feeding would be astonished and horrified if they were able to be present at psychiatric sessions in which the patient under treatment reproduces feelings and impressions of terror of being pursued and attacked with a terrible weapon which is going to pin him down, transfix or even kill him. This process is being carried out by a mother or mother-substitute with the best of motives, who is convinced that the baby needs food, and that her task is to force the teat into his mouth by any means available, whether he resists or not.

It should be realized, however, that these disabilities— timidity, shrinking, disgust, etc. of the mother in respect of breast-feeding are symptoms, and the condition is amenable to psychological treatment. Until this has been tried breast-feeding should not be abandoned as hopeless. Admittedly, it is highly desirable that such treatment should be given before childbirth.

Now, it will be urged that this is all very well but there are women who cannot possibly feed their babies however much they want to, because they have no milk. In fact, obstetricians have been heard to make the remark, ' You either have milk or you haven't.' Now it has been stated by competent authorities* that any woman who is healthy enough to produce a live baby can also feed it. This, of course, will be denied in many quarters. It would perhaps be better to extend the statement of the authority quoted above and say that she *can* feed it if she loves the baby and really wants to feed it. But this want must be genuine and real, and is not equivalent to a statement that she wants to do so. It must be true in her unconscious as well as her conscious. In other words, this inability to feed the baby on account of absence

* Joyce Partridge, *Baby's Point of View*: Prof. Marfan, Prof. Pinard, of Paris; *Truby King, The Man*, p. 166.

of milk is in itself an emotional disorder, curable by psychotherapy; but of course it would be undesirable to start this treatment after the baby is born. There is little doubt that simple encouragement, coupled with psychotherapy, would help considerably in many of such cases, but too often instead of this they are discouraged, and this discouragement reinforces their own unconscious wish to escape from what they regard as a task instead of a privilege.

There are more things that a psychiatrist can say about this matter of breast-feeding and its importance, though these statements are likely to be received with scepticism and incredulity. For example, it has been stated that if a competent psychiatrist has the opportunity of observing a breast-feeding relationship over a long enough period of time, he will be able to prophesy with some confidence what the future development of that baby is likely to be. In particular, he will be able to form an idea of how the individual will behave when it comes to marital relationship in adult life. A little reflection will show the close similarity between breast-feeding and adult coitus. In both there is or should be a preliminary approach of courtship or wooing, a reciprocal and mutual activity and enjoyment, a crescendo leading up to what must be called an orgasm in both cases, with satiety, relaxation and composure, and in the case of the baby at least, sleep. The difference clearly lies in the type of personality involved. In the case of breast-feeding it is, or is presumed to be, a mature adult and an infant; in the case of adult coitus it is presumed to be an affair of two mature adults.

The psychiatrist is himself astonished to find that the pattern which is established in breast-feeding is frequently repeated when it comes to adult life. That is to say, that if breast-feeding was accompanied by dissatisfaction, frustration, fear, guilt, etc., these reactions reappear in the adult relationship.

Such difficulties as impotence, frigidity, some sterility, vaginismus, premature ejaculation can be traced back to situations in the first year of life. This may seem more credible if we remind ourselves that both the breast-feeding relationship and the adult relationship are essentially relationships between persons and that the breast-feeding relationship is for the baby, as we have elsewhere suggested, the first social relationship, the first sensuous relationship, and the first love relationship.

Even in logic, therefore, it would not be unreasonable to suppose that this might set the pattern for all subsequent relationships of the same type.

12.—FRIGIDITY

EARLIER in discussing inadequacy in a mother's capacity to nurse her baby I described such attitudes as timidity, apprehension, disgust, etc. and suggested that together they formed an attitude of 'frigidity' towards the baby. This is not a customary application of the term frigidity: it usually refers to an attitude of coldness, aloofness, indifference or hostility towards a mate regarding conjugal intercourse. But I believe the above is a legitimate and logical use of the term, because the two situations are related to one another and largely depend upon one another. Where frigidity occurs in the breast-feeding situation there is (in the mother) an incapacity to respond to the infant with appropriate sensuous feelings and consequently the mammary function is interfered with or inhibited. Since such feelings are founded upon instinct there must be conflict present and the appropriate reactions are unavailable because of repression. In the conjugal situation it is chiefly genital feeling that is repressed. In both cases, then, sensuous feelings are repressed and unavailable for function. But we must be careful to discriminate here between true pathological frigidity and apparent frigidity, or (otherwise expressed) between absolute frigidity and relative frigidity. For example, it is natural for a woman to be frigid towards a man she dislikes, even if he be her husband. We cannot regard this as maladjusted or morbid. Unfortunately women do sometimes marry men whom they fundamentally dislike (just as men sometimes marry women with whom they will be naturally impotent). In the conjugal situation, then, we cannot regard frigidity in the woman as abnormal or neurotic unless we know something of the relationship existing. It would be necessary to ascertain that there was some man towards whom she was not frigid. It is when a woman is frigid towards a husband she appears to love that we may assume a psychopathological explanation. In this case the frigidity may be absolute. (But we must not ignore the fact that some women are frigid towards men they love—professedly—and actively aroused by men they dislike or are disgusted by. To discuss this would take us too far away from our theme. It is clearly again relative frigidity.)

In only some cases of conjugal frigidity, then, is the condition abnormal: whereas all cases where the mother is frigid towards her baby in breast-feeding must be regarded as morbid (psychopathological). If we are to alleviate the condition of conjugal frigidity we must seek for its source and origin. Since the instincts involved are strong it is clear that strong opposing forces are at work. We may assume that these are the familiar ones of fear, guilt and disgust. These emotions, however, will not necessarily be conscious in the subject. For such a profound disturbance to be produced we would suspect that the disturbance originated at a time when the personality was in a sensitive and formative stage—namely, in infancy or early childhood. And this is just what we discover. In the course of treatment we are repeatedly provided with evidence that this conjugal frigidity has its source in infancy in an unsatisfactory breast-feeding relationship. Here there has been frustration and deprivation, partial or total, with resulting conflict and repression of oral sensuous feeling (in Freudian terms 'oral sexuality'). This conflict and repression and consequent failure in personal relationship is repeated two decades later in the analogous conjugal relationship. Stating this in its crudest form one might say that an infant who never succeeded in obtaining oral satisfaction at the breast of her mother may later also be incapable of vaginal satisfaction with her husband. Not only may there be lack of satisfaction but also apparent total lack of desire: for a strong desire which cannot be satisfied is an intolerable state.

This must not be taken to mean that genital or conjugal frigidity invariably follows deprivation in the first year or that there are no other contributory factors: nor must it be taken to mean that such frigidity is the only possible result of first year deprivation.

It may be difficult for some to accept the close causal connection between oral deprivation in the first year and vaginal frigidity twenty or more years later. But the transition from one receptive organ (the mouth) to another receptive organ (the vagina) is not psychologically difficult. The essence of the problem is not concerned with organs or particular orifices. The essential problem is that of an intimate sensuous relationship (love relationship) with another person —a 'copulative' one in both cases; it is this that, having failed in the first year, cannot be established in the later one. It can be said with confidence that, if a baby (female) is adequately breast-fed and thus achieves a complete and satisfactory sensuous relationship with her mother, she will not be frigid as a wife—provided that she does not marry a man she dislikes.

We must therefore return to the inadequate, timid, shrinking or disgusted mother whom we described as frigid: for she is responsible for the deprivation in her baby and for the latter's possible consequent conjugal frigidity. But it is unjust and unprofitable to condemn or blame the mother: unless it be one of the rarer cases of deliberate neglect, her frigidity is not of her choosing, but is a disability for which again she is not responsible: it is probably a result of failure in her own nurture. Thus the trouble proceeds from generation to generation. If this seems a somewhat depressing tale it should be mentioned that both types of frigidity can be successfully treated. Clearly it is desirable that treatment should be undertaken before childbirth in the one case and before marriage in the other.

Some women who are frigid suppose that the condition is inherent as a natural endowment. They may even regard it as a virtue and evidence of chastity. But such a view is biologically and psychologically false. Unless there is some gross physical illness or defect or some surgical removal, the frigidity is a symptom or sign of psychic disturbance. If, however, the subject is content with the condition it may be difficult to treat. Commonly, however, there are other symptoms connected with it though the connection is not recognized by the patient. It will be evident that frigidity (when morbid as indicated) is usually associated with other signs of emotional immaturity, and is commonly also associated with other symptoms of neurosis.

The subject of frigidity, somewhat neglected in the past, is now rightly receiving more attention. By some it has been regarded as an affair concerning one individual alone: its importance lies in the fact that it breaks a relationship involving two persons. If the wife is frigid the husband is dissatisfied and frustrated whether impotent or not. Frigidity reduces the possibility of pregnancy; but there is no doubt that many apparently frigid women become pregnant.

The above discussion is not intended as a complete dissertation on the subject of frigidity, but as an indication of its relationship to infant nurture which is our particular theme. Many important considerations are omitted, as for example the attitude of the mate or husband in promoting or mitigating a frigid attitude.

We have mentioned these disabilities—impotence, frigidity, etc. here because they have a specific connection with the marital relationship and with reproduction; but it must not be supposed that disorders resulting from disturbances in the first year are limited to symptoms of this type. This would be a false impression. Many of the protean manifestations of emotional disorder and neurosis have their source in the first year. If the symptoms are predominantly psychic they generally interfere with social relationships, so that indirectly they may interfere with marriage or conjugal adjustment. Sometimes the symptoms are predominantly physical and it is this type of illness which is now referred to as psycho-somatic disorder. As might be expected, gastric disturbances and disturbances of digestion are common here.

At this point it might be appropriate to explain something of the mechanisms that operate in the mind of a person who has suffered from these unfortunate experiences in the first year. As referred to previously, the disturbances result from the thwarting or frustration of the needs of the infant for protective or sensuous love. We must attempt to describe what happens in the child's mind as the result of this. He is endowed with this instinctual urge and is deprived of the satisfaction of it. This may represent such an intolerable situation that he may turn away from it, as it were, so that later he avoids it in consciousness as if it did not exist. This is in crude outline the mechanism which psychiatrists call repression. These instinctual urges are now said to be repressed, and do not appear in consciousness. The subject is unaware of their existence as such. But by being repressed they do not cease to exist; in fact, they remain very much alive and active in the unconscious part of the mind. But it is important to note that they remain exactly in the form in which they were at the time of the repression, which in the case we are considering, means the form appropriate to the first year; and this situation persists into adult life, so that the original instinctual urges are still seeking satisfaction in their primitive and original mode, but are not recognized as such in consciousness; their activity is only manifested in a devious manner by symptoms whose connection with them is not obvious to the ordinary observer nor to the subject who suffers them. Consequently, we have a person who is physiologically and intellectually adult but whose emotional and social adaptation is inadequate and whose sensuous needs are those appropriate to an infant of the first year. It is sometimes supposed that repression of some instinctual urge disposes of it or nullifies it. This is an error; it remains just as strong and active (though unconscious) as it was originally, but on account of the conflict and repression with which it becomes involved, it usually is not directly manifested in consciousness. On the other hand, when these urges and needs in the first year are satisfied, i.e. when the mother's attitude is healthy and adequate, the urges cease to operate in this original and primitive form, but progress towards more mature forms. Thus if unsatisfied and repressed they remain clamant, primitive and unchanged: if satisfied, they develop and no longer demand satisfaction in their original form.

13.—FAILURE OF MOTHERHOOD

IF we now summarize the foregoing discussion in the form of a broad thesis, this will be that a great deal of the emotional disturbance and neurosis that we observe is the result of a failure of motherhood in our generation. It must therefore be our concern to examine the causes of this failure. Women have not lost their maternal instinct but it has been overlaid and distorted by indoctrination of various kinds, some derived from religious sources and some from pseudo-science. It would be most unjust to blame the women. They are the victims of a culture, and one of the purposes of this book is to suggest to women that they should cherish and rely upon their instinctive feelings towards the infant, and allow these feelings free course.

As an example of the type of teaching to which women are subjected, we would quote the following as one among many. A film was recently produced by the British Ministry of Health entitled " Your Children and You." Its purpose is to give advice on healthy nurture of children. The film illustrates various scenes from early infancy to later childhood and is accompanied by a running commentary of advice. Referring to the first few months of life, the film portrays scenes which leave the impression that the care of a baby at this time is a tremendous burden on both parents, and even a nuisance to the neighbours. It speaks of the mother as a slave, and while implying that up to a point this is inevitable, the commentator says, ' But the slave has got to start right away teaching the family rules. If not, your life won't be worth living.' It is presumably the baby of three weeks who must be taught the family rules. This is in accordance with much similar teaching which has held sway in our generation, and is unfortunately very insidious because it is specious.

It suggests that the baby represents a potential threat to the rest of the family, that he may become a tyrant unless measures are taken to correct this; that he needs disciplining from the very beginning. The underlying theory is that since · he is going to grow up into a world in which he cannot have everything he wants, he must learn this in the first few weeks.

This theory is both fallacious and pernicious. It is true that later on he will find that he cannot have all that he wants. But if in the early months his urgent needs are satisfied he will accept the later situation. If deprived, he will continue to have infantile needs and wants in adult life. The doctrine further suggests that the infant has some sinister anti-social or aggressive tendencies towards dominating his environment which must be cured from the start. Such a view is both grave and naïve: it shows a complete ignorance of the real nature of the child at this age, and completely ignores his absolute helplessness and dependence, his intense need for security and for the sensuous satisfaction of the breast.

and his extreme liability to fear. Expressed otherwise, the doctrine suggests that the baby is in some way a danger to the peace of the household, even a potential enemy.

If carried out, this means a continual competition or war between the baby and the mother which the infant begins to sense very early. Consequently, he feels it vitally necessary to defend himself and satisfy his urgent needs in th best way he can, which will be by crying and screaming.

Unfortunately this doctrine has gained credence, and a large number of babies are subjected to it. As a result, in very truth a war is set up between mother and child, and becomes a permanent relationship in which the mother has a perpetual problem of how to discipline the child, how to get it to do what she wants. The child feels that he must fight to survive in a hostile world. Thus a friendly love relationship between mother and child—on which all further development depends—is broken at the very beginning. A child then does veritably become a tyrant. The remedy usually applied is to supply more discipline. There are now two possibilities open. One is more discipline or nagging, which will make matters worse, and the child more obstinate; the other is that if the discipline is severe enough, the child may be intimidated and surrender, and become submissive and obedient. He is now a neurotic and will need to be supported and looked after by someone for the rest of his life.

The explanation that will be offered for this unfortunate result is that he should have been disciplined more. This is the opposite of the true explanation, which is that the child should have been loved and protected, and *not* disciplined *in the first year*. At the time the film was shown we published a commentary on it. and it is perhaps relevant to reproduce part of it here:

' The film begins by depicting the situation in the first year as if the baby were a burden to the parents. It also suggests that there is necessarily some kind of competition between the baby and the mother for power, or domination. or mastery, and that it is desirable for the mother to win this battle. These attitudes taken together represent a disastrously inadequate attitude on the part of the mother to a child at that age. Unfortunately. it depicts a situation that often does occur. but. in the interests of the mental health

of the child, it would really be better from the child's point
of view if such parents did not have children at all. It
would be preferable if the opening note were that expressed
in a sentence that occurs later in the film, namely " The
child must have the certainty of your love." That is clearly
not possible if there exists some competition or struggle
for mastery. There is no reference at all to the vital mother-
child relationship during the breast-feeding period in the
first six or nine months, upon which so many later stages
of development depend. If the mother, instead of loving the
child, feels there is a danger of his becoming a tyrant—
in other words, becomes anxious about this—a struggle or
war undoubtedly *will* start. This will prejudice all future
relationships between mother and child.'

As regards the term ' slave ' applied to the mother. The
question is whether she is a happy devoted slave, and enjoys
being in this manner a slave more than anything else in the
world, or whether she resents the situation as an encroachment
upon her freedom and her other activities. At this point we
might justifiably refer again to the higher mammals. If one
observed cats or dogs during the nursing period, they could,
from one point of view, be considered as slaves, but it would
be absurd to suggest that they resent it or are unhappy in the
situation. If it be contended that women are not animals
and therefore should not be expected to behave in the same
way as animal mothers, we would agree, in the sense that
human mothers should be able to be superior, not inferior, to
the higher mammals. We are also taking it for granted that
the supreme object to be considered is the ultimate mental
health of the child.

14.—CONFIRMATIONS

SINCE I began writing this book and actually while I was
writing these preceding passages (October 1948) there has
come into my hands in most timely fashion a very interesting
publication, *The Lesson of Okinawa*, by Newton Dillaway.
Such statements as I have been making as a psychiatrist are
frequently received with scepticism, and the hearer demands
proof of their validity. This proof is difficult to supply unless

the questioner has special opportunities for investigation or has special powers of discernment. In this book, *The Lesson of Okinawa*, there is a report of a community homogeneous enough and isolated enough to constitute, as it were, a laboratory experiment. It is a lesson in mental hygiene derived from the culture of the Okinawans. The author quotes from Dr. J. C. Moloney of Detroit thus:

' This psychological stamina stems from the excellent start the Okinawan child gets in life. He is well mothered.'

The author, Mr. Dillaway, proceeds:

' Dr. Moloney believes that the " permissive " method employed by the Okinawan mother is a basic factor in establishing a foundation of emotional stability. The Okinawan baby is offered the breast whenever hungry, and often when frightened. The latter is important because nursing during a fear state comforts a baby, allays his anxieties, affords him a sense of security and gives him confidence in the protective powers of his mother. This is conducive to a healthy psychological maturation. During these early days of life fear states, if allowed to persist, can warp emotional development. Allowed to continue in a state of fear, the child develops an aggravated apprehension of the outer world, and he loses his sense of security and his sense of the protective powers of his mother. Consequently he develops neurotic techniques of mastery.'—(*The Lesson of Okinawa*, pp. 14 and 15.)

I have quoted at length from this book, *The Lesson of Okinawa*, because, if this language be compared with some that I have written, a remarkable degree of congruity will be observed. It should be noted that my conclusions are derived from a long experience of effort, designed to undo the troubles resulting from early nurture; while the evidence quoted is derived from the observation of the results of the type of nurture recommended, in a community which seems to have a common practice. In beginning to write I had not anticipated such valuable confirmation as Mr. Dillaway and Dr. Moloney have supplied. It should be further noted in reference to Dr. Moloney's contention that, if the baby is to be offered the breast whenever hungry and often when frightened, he (the baby) must be in constant and close association with the mother. Also since beginning to write the book there have been other encouraging signs. Dr. Spence of Newcastle, England, has been touring Australia and New Zealand and has strongly advocated a close association of mother and baby, whether in the hospital or in the home. Dr. Grantly Dick Read has rendered a valuable contribution in advocating normal childbirth—that is, childbirth without narcosis, and of this we shall have more to say later. As far as I myself am concerned, I wish to emphasize again that these opinions I have expressed about child nurture are not the result of reflective musings upon the subject or evolved out of my inner consciousness, but the result of things heard and seen by myself with patients in the consulting room. These things are impressions of distressing and disturbing experiences in infancy and early childhood, and the reproduction of them is also distressing to the patient. They are impressions of insecurity, of deprivation, of loneliness, of frustration, of being neglected or unloved; the disturbing emotions experienced are those of fear, rage, hate, aggressiveness and guilt. These patients are adults and they are reproducing experiences beyond the range of normal memory. The question, then, is frequently asked as to how such impressions can be reliable. The best answer that can be given to this is that if the questioner could be present at such interviews he would be convinced of their reliability. It is not always possible to test them against historical fact, but when this is possible the degree of conformity is remarkable. It should be noted that most of the mothers of these patients are not at all vicious people but are convinced of their good intentions toward the baby. This is an example of the fact that it is not enough in this matter of child nurture to have good intentions. The point here is that all of them fail to carry out the type of nurture which apparently is the custom in Okinawa. Many of them are quite unfitted for the task of motherhood.

15.—EMOTIONAL MATURITY

WE have offered the proposition that a great deal of the illness and maladjustment of people in the Anglo-Saxon culture is due to a failure of motherhood. We suggested th' this was partly due to indoctrination. But indoctrination alone received in adult life is not powerful enough in itself to have these serious effects. The maternal instinct is strong, and something more than indoctrination is necessary to interfere with its operation. We can regard the life of an individual as being of two stages—childhood and maturity, with the transitional stage of adolescence. The essential feature of childhood is the need for protection and love, while the criterion of an adult is the capacity to stand on his or her own feet, and more than this, to be able to support children as well. One might extend this conception to say that the mature adult should exhibit the following qualities:

1. A capacity for friendship.
2. Adequate courage.
3. Self-confidence.
4. A capacity to be a good parent.
5. A capacity to love someone outside himself or herself.

Now while most children if given food and shelter grow in stature and become adult in the physical sense, and, if given a conventional education, may develop their intellects, they do not all, by virtue of receiving these things, develop the five emotional qualities just mentioned and thus become emotionally mature adults. They may be physically mature and emotionally childish or immature. In contradistinction to the above five qualities, the emotionally immature person will usually display a lack of self-confidence, timidity, incapacity to take responsibility, inability to make friendships of an adult type, and a lack of capacity to love. In the matter of lack of self-confidence, this quality may be masked if the person concerned is protected by a family constellation or similar community. It is necessary to expatiate somewhat on what is meant by a capacity for love. The infant has a very great need for love; it could be said he has a very great capacity for receiving love, and this need must be supplied. A characteristic of the emotionally mature adult is that while he is ready and able to receive love he will not break down without this; at the same time he has a desire to give or provide love to other persons, adults or children. The emotionally immature person on the other hand will tend to need the support or love of some parental figure, though this need may be heavily disguised. So that the word *love*, though it has a common basis of feeling, should mean different things in the infant and in the adult. It is necessary to consider the conditions under which a person develops from *the need to be loved* in infancy to the *capacity to love* in adults.

As explained earlier, if the individual is adequately loved in infancy and early childhood he will normally develop this capacity by the end of adolescence. If he is not loved and protected in infancy the infantile craving remains unsatisfied and, especially if it becomes involved in conflict and repression, continues into adult life in its original form as a need to be loved. Much so-called 'falling in love' is of this character.

A further difficulty arises from the fact that an immature person who is otherwise (intellectually and physically) adult is unable to appreciate this situation or to distinguish this feeling from normal adult love. The psycho-analysts call this capacity to love *object love*, which means a capacity to love another person, infant or adult *as he is*, with the sum total of his physical and mental qualities. This is the type of love which the infant needs to receive; it is inadequate to say ' I love my child very much but I wish he had not got red hair or splayed ears.'

We have intentionally stressed the importance of nurture for fostering adult love in the personality, but we would be guilty of exaggeration if we made no allowance for the operation of another factor, viz., the hereditary or constitutional one. It must be granted that people vary in constitutional endowment, and if we consider two people both of whom have received adequate nurture one may reach a higher level of emotional maturity than the other because of these inherent qualities of endowment. There is also evidence to suggest that in women natural childbirth and motherhood are culminating factors in producing emotional maturity. Emotional maturity and mental health are equivalent terms. but we cannot so equate emotional immaturity and neurosis. All persons suffering from a neurosis will be emotionally immature. but the converse is not necessarily true. The question whether the emotionally immature person is neurotic will depend upon a number of other factors such as the presence or absence of conflict. the presence or absence of external stress, and the nature of the personal environment surrounding him.

We have stressed the importance of early nurture for producing healthy personalities, and have said that mental health in the adult is equivalent to emotional maturity. If early nurture is inadequate in the ways we have described it tends to produce neurosis or emotional immaturity or both, and since the greatest tests of emotional maturity occur in relation to mating and parenthood, it is essentially in this sphere that the emotionally immature person fails. It is clear, then, that a person who has been deprived of adequate nurture in infancy will tend to be an inadequate parent in his or her turn and repeat the process. This is another way of saying that neurosis is infectious or contagious, that it is handed on from one generation to another. It is commonly supposed that this recurrence of neurosis in a succession of generations is due to heredity. We have referred to this question before. There is no doubt that a susceptibility (which we have elsewhere referred to as the tender or sensitive type) is hereditary but it will not tend to neurosis in the presence of adequate nurture. This statement is substantiated by the fact that if a person so suffering receive adequate psychological treatment, this may compensate, sometimes completely, for his inadequate nurture, and he then becomes emotionally mature and able to become a good parent and the vicious chain is broken.

It is sometimes said that in order to be mentally healthy it is necessary to have good parents and that this is particularly difficult to arrange! This somewhat dismal proposition must be held true in the absence of provision for adequate treatment, but it also emphasizes the fact that the importance of early nurture in producing healthy individuals extends beyond the span of an individual life. This again appears to be observable in operation in Okinawa. But not only in Okinawa, for there are good parents among Anglo-Saxons.

There will be women who will say, ' I am not willing to turn back the clock and become primitive or native in order to produce healthy children.' I have known women who have remarked in regard to breast-feeding that they are not going to turn themselves into a cow. This contention must be met. Clearly there must be a fallacy in it, because if the progress of such a civilization or culture results in the production of increasing numbers of mentally unhealthy persons, the future for our civilization is dark, and it is liable to be superseded by a culture of another creed or colour. But the fallacy lies in the supposition that civilization and culture cannot develop concurrently with adequate motherhood, including the full operation of the maternal instinct in the 'primitive' form. In fact, our contention is that only thus can social progress and culture proceed. The fallacy lies in accepting false standards of values.

Here we may return to the importance of indoctrination. It is clear that indoctrination will be more effective with people who are suggestible and this is a characteristic of the emotionally immature. Indoctrination, then, will be potent in intensifying the disability of the emotionally immature.

Loving the Child

In the section on Mental Hygiene and Nurture we said that the essential principle was that 'the child must be loved.' In the above section on emotional maturity we have examined some of the possible meanings of the word 'love.' People writing on child management and nurture frequently assert that a child can be *overloved* and that this may lead to 'spoiling.'

One feels sorry for the anxious parent who is seeking guidance and who is told that the child must be loved but that it is dangerous to overlove him.

What is the truth about this matter?

I believe that the difficulty arises from confusion in regard to the meaning of the word 'love.' I think a good case could be made for the proposition that it is the most abused word in the language.

We have said that 'the child must be " loved " '; and, if it be the *child* that is loved for his own sake, I am certain that it is impossible to love him too much. No existing parent is sufficiently emotionally mature to love the child enough to produce his maximum capacity for mental health. The view that the child can be overloved arises from the fact that many parents who have a *feeling* of love, and who believe that they are loving the child are in fact not doing so but loving themselves, and loving the child as a possession or as an extension of themselves. The parent who cannot bear to let

38

the child of three out of her sight, the parent who can never
allow the child to try any enterprise or adventure for fear
he might hurt himself, the parent who cannot bear to incur
the child's anger by saying ' No ' when necessary—these are
not examples of loving the child, but of loving oneself. There
is no doubt that harm can be done by emotionally immature
parents who suppose that they love the child, when, in fact,
they are needing his love for their own satisfaction.

This, I think, is the explanation of the view that the child
can be overloved. I am convinced that he cannot be. It is
most desirable that people who make assertions about love
should be clear in their minds as to what kind of love is involved, and as to who the person is, that, in fact, is loved.

16.—WEANING

How long should breast-feeding go on? When should the
child be weaned? These are questions that are constantly
asked. Most authorities are agreed that it should be at least
six months. If the question asks for a general rule as to the
length of time in weeks or months that breast-feeding should
continue beyond the minimum six months, the answer is that
no such rule could or should be given. We would emphasize
again that the situation here is a personal relationship. Therefore such questions as these can only be decided by the two
parties concerned: the mother and the baby together. Supposing an engaged couple came to a physician and asked for
an opinion as to how often they should kiss one another, the
physician would probably decline to answer. This is perhaps
not a fair parallel, but it illustrates the principle. If in the
early months the baby should be fed when he wants to be, so
in general he should continue to be fed as long as he wants
to be; and under healthy conditions the mother will want to
feed him as long as this need exists. Under healthy conditions
the mother will be able to discern this need and also the signs
that he wants to proceed to the next phase. There is, however,
a possible factor here about which care must be exercised. It
is possible that the mother may wish to prolong breast-feeding
for her own gratification (and perhaps protection) past the
time when the child has any real need. This would be an
exploitation of the baby involving the motive to keep him

permanently as a suckling. Experience tends to show that under healthy conditions, i.e. after at least six months of satisfactory suckling, the child will earlier or later exhibit a desire to bite or chew on solid material and thus be ready to wean himself. The time when this desire shows itself will vary between, say, six months to fifteen months. It is hardly necessary to state that weaning should be a gradual process, as this is now widely recognized. The psychiatrist finds from experience that active or too early weaning or abrupt weaning is likely to have serious effects on the development of the child. We would state again that if the breast-feeding period has involved a really satisfactory relationship, the baby is not only content to relinquish it, being satisfied, but wishes to proceed to the next stage: if the relationship has been unsatisfactory the baby may want to prolong this situation indefinitely, always in the hope of obtaining satisfaction, and such a wish may persist into adult life, in more or less disguised form. This, then, will constitute some kind of ' perversion.'

17.—PROBLEMS OF THE SECOND YEAR

So far we have been almost entirely preoccupied with the nature of the child in the first year, and the corresponding nurture. The problems of the second year are different and it is undesirable that any one should suppose that the principles already enunciated apply in all respects to the second year. The child does not grow uniformly and homogeneously like a crystal or a carrot, but by stages or phases which succeed one another and which differ from one another. Just as in the first year the child is dependent and helpless and feels so, so, in the second year, when he has got vertical and mobile, he is actually less dependent and helpless, and feels powerful and independent—in fact, may have a feeling that he is lord of all he surveys. This is a complete reversal of phase from the situation in the first year. Even as adults we are aware of a marked difference in feeling between the vertical and horizontal positions. This arrogance and assertiveness is a normal attitude of mind and should be allowed freedom to develop. This does not mean that when he demands the moon it should be brought to him; but he should be allowed, as far as is safe and convenient to the rest of the family, to go and get things he wants, or attempt to do so, including the moon. It is not desirable or necessary to make frantic efforts to satisfy all his demands or wants, nor is it desirable to stand in his way more than is absolutely necessary for convenience and safety. If male, he may become very aggressive and truculent—this must be regarded as a healthy attitude and not as naughtiness, though again it is desirable to prevent him by force if necessary from hurting other people, especially children. But force means *restraint*, not punishment. It is essential to avoid giving him the impression that these truculent tendencies are wicked.

These are conditions which will apply if the first year has been healthy, but what if it has not? What will happen if in the first year a war has been set up between mother and child? Now that he has become vertical, mobile and active and feels powerful and independent, he will be disposed to get his own back—perhaps seek revenge. And he may exploit this situation to the limit. Again, this must be held to be the healthiest reaction he can exhibit in these circumstances. The actual time period at which the child passes from the phase of dependence and helplessness to aggressiveness and independence varies between 15 months to 2 years, and the phase itself, while it is limited, may vary between one and two years. That is to say, that under healthy conditions this aggressive period usually finishes about the age of 3 when the child enters a second *dependent* phase. But this is of a different type from the dependence of the first year. Now the child begins to realize that there are other *persons* in the world than himself and they must be taken into consideration, and also that it is desirable to be on good terms with them. This is the beginning of social behaviour. For the present, however, we are concerned with the preceding phase of assertiveness or aggressiveness which occurs between the ages of 1½ to 3 years.

18.—BOWEL TRAINING

It is during this period that training in cleanliness, or bowel training, is usually begun. As this process is very critical for the subsequent health of the child, we must include some discussion of it here. In the first year the centre of sensuous experience for the child is the mouth. When the child has developed a capacity to bite and chew and to feed himself with his hands, this focussing of sensuous experience in the mouth declines in importance, having fulfilled its function of establishing nutrition.

The next function to be established is that of excretion, including defaecation and micturition; and now in accordance with this need the corresponding organs—the anus and the urethra, become the supreme centres of sensuous experience, and remain so until their functions are securely established. Expressed otherwise, the performance of these functions be-comes the child's dominant interest; that is, provided that the first year has been satisfactorily accomplished. Consequently, the child naturally desires to urinate and defaecate at that time and in that place which gives him the greatest satisfaction. If he is to become an acceptable member of society he will have to learn to renounce these desires, at least to a consider-able extent—that is, become less natural and more social—therefore some kind of bowel training or education is neces-sary. The important question is, how best can this be accomplished?

The first fact of importance here is that it is dangerous to the mental health of the child to begin this process too early, or to exert too much pressure at any stage. As well as being dangerous to mental health, it would also tend to defeat its purposes, viz., to promote psychologically healthy and also socially acceptable bowel function. Those nurses and mothers who vie with one another in getting their child ' clean ' as they say, at the earliest possible time, are a danger to the child's health. It is far better to delay the process until such time as the child will be willing to co-operate. At about the age of three (as mentioned earlier) the child begins to develop a social sense—a desire to imitate grown-up people. He will seek to do what grown-up people do, and if he has an opportunity of observing adults in this matter he will wish to imitate them, first as regards place and later as regards time. It is dangerous, therefore, to apply pressure too soon, whether this be in the form of warnings or threats or even rewards. This function must not be made into a moral issue with the child. He must not be called ' good ' if he defaecates at the time and place that the parent wishes, or 'naughty' if he doesn't. We said earlier that if a war had started with the mother in the first year it would probably become intense in the second, since the child is not now helpless and sees the opportunity for revenge. No opportunity of defiance and revenge is superior to that of bowel function. You can take a horse to the water but you cannot make him drink. You can take a child to the pot but you cannot make him defaecate; neither can all the king's horses and all the king's men. The child is aware of this and exploits it with great satisfaction. The greater the entreaty or coaxing the stronger the resistance. If instead of coaxing and entreating, threats and punishment are used and the child frightened, the situation becomes more complicated and he may now be unable to defaecate although he needs to do so and outwardly wishes to.

It is important, therefore, that this self-willedness have freedom of expression. The phrase 'freedom of expression' should perhaps be explained. It is essential that the child be not threatened or frightened or punished or made to feel guilty because he is self-willed. It is for him a normal phase of development; but it requires great delicacy of handling. But 'freedom of expression' does not mean that adults are compelled to gratify all his wishes or that he must be allowed to burn the house down if that is his will. If this self-willedness is punished or threatened and thus overlaid with feelings of guilt, it may never develop, and the person concerned will, as an adult, suffer from indecision and lack of confidence and exhibit self-willedness or obstinacy and lack of initiative and capacity for leadership; i.e., he will lack 'will' in the adult sense. It is important to note that this self-willed phase is normally temporary and transient and will disappear about the age of three.

It is not suggested that merely to hold a child over a pot even during the first year is necessarily dangerous; the essential principle is again that of the relationship between mother and child. During this period the child not only enjoys his own bowel and urinary functions but wants his mother to share in his enjoyment. If the mother is able to do this, and if a good relationship has developed in the first year, then the problem of bowel training will present little difficulty or danger. There is even some disadvantage in writing books

43

of this type in that there is a possibility that good mothers who have an excellent relationship with the child, and are managing the situation spontaneously and naturally, may become anxious as to whether they are doing the right thing. This book is not written for them. They may hold the baby over the pot as early as the age of one year in an atmosphere of fun which both enjoy together. They will desist if the baby shows resistance or fear. The danger arises in the cases —and they are many—where the relationship in the first year has not been good and a war exists. Here the mother will feel she must not be defeated, and will show anxiety, irritability, perhaps anger and disgust. We have been concerned to emphasize the great importance of the mother-child relationship in the first year and to indicate that all the subsequent stages of development and management become difficult if it has failed.

Another of the rules stated by Joyce Partridge in *Baby's Point of View* is worth quoting here. It is 'Never scold a baby and never allow anyone else to scold him for wetting or soiling napkins or for wetting or soiling any other place whatsoever.' Expressed otherwise, this means that it is essential to avoid giving the child a sense of guilt about these natural functions.

19.—MORAL TRAINING

ONE of the most remarkable discoveries of analytical psychology is that 'moral training' is dangerous for young children. Since the acquisition of a real morality is of great importance for everyone, this finding may seem disconcerting. 'Moral Training' will include the use of the terms 'wicked.' 'naughty,' 'sinful,' 'disgusting.' These words should never be used to a child. But 'moral training' may also begin before the language period through corresponding facial expressions and gestures.

An excellent example of what is meant by this kind of 'moral training' is given by Braithwaite in *Parent and Child* and I propose to quote it. He quotes an extract issued for the guidance of those who have the guardianship of young children:

'"However young the child may be, it is never too early to begin to lead aright the little life. The outcome of original sin will be seen in the perversity, temper and selfishness of the small child. A wise teacher will deal with such an offence and not say that it does not matter because he is so young. The first wrong-doing must be dealt with: a grieved look, or a few minutes in the corner will probably be sufficient." '

The sanctimonious air is apparent. Braithwaite states that this is derived from an ecclesiastical source. When the author says ' a grieved look or a few minutes in the corner will be sufficient ' he means sufficient to produce a feeling of fear and guilt that he thinks desirable. The following is Braithwaite's comment:

' No words can better sum up the treatment to which the child (the sacred trust) should be subjected if it is the intention of the guardians to create the most abnormal conflicts and repressions in their charge. In a word, the child is to be regarded as the " outcome of original sin " instead of perfect for the purposes of its coming life. Having once accepted this view of the child, it is only logical that we should proceed to eradicate its imperfections. Such a course will be easier than cultivation. Cultivation requires love and service. The creation of repression needs only self-love and tyranny.'

The type of morality produced by such treatment will be that of obedience to ' moral law ' on the basis of fear. John Macmurray has pointed out that such a morality is not suitable for human beings and, in fact, is not a true human morality. He further explains that despite all the talk about it, there is no such thing as a ' moral law.' (*Freedom in the Modern World*, John Macmurray.) True human morality will be based on friendship, co-operation and love. A morality based on obedience or fear may be expedient for a primitive people but only a true human morality will be appropriate for a true democracy or an association of free people. In order, then, to produce true morality in young children we must love them: apart from this their moral standard will be based upon our own, by imitation.

20.—DISCIPLINE

ONE is frequently asked in relation to all the foregoing,
' What provision do you make for discipline and obedience?
Surely it is important that the child should learn both discipline and obedience. You say that the child must be loved
and must not be frustrated. This presumably means that the
child is to have his own way in everything. Surely this will
make for a spoilt child? ' We must try to meet this difficulty.
It is important to emphasize at the outset that loving a child
is not the same as indulging him. It is commonly supposed
that ' spoiling ' is due to too much love. Actually the reverse
is the case. The parent who feels unable to love the child
adequately, tries to compensate for this by giving the child
presents and gratifying every whim; the child's wants increase
indefinitely in this direction because his primary need for
real affection is unsatisfied. Also the emotionally immature
parent is dependent on the child's approval and cannot bear
to say ' No ' to him. From the second year onwards the child
should come in contact as far as possible with the real world
(including, if possible, other children) in which he will find
there are things that he wants that he cannot have. things that
he wants to do that he cannot do. It is good for him to learn
these frustrations in the real world: the parent may well
sympathize with his distress, but if she attempts to solve these
problems for him (which ultimately means procuring the
moon), she is not serving the best interests of the child. and
will get into difficulties herself.

The word ' discipline ' is difficult. In common usage it has
no precise meaning. There is the discipline of an army; there
is the discipline of learning a musical instrument; there is
the discipline of a school class where, if the class is quiet
and orderly. the teacher is said to be a good disciplinarian.
We speak also of an undisciplined person. What is vitally
necessary for the child to learn is self-discipline, but parents
frequently equate discipline with obedience and think that all
is well if the child is submissive to all commands and prohibitions, and that he is then disciplined. Actually it will be
seen that such a process is in some measure incompatible with
the development of true self-discipline. Is, then, obedience
not to be sought? The answer is that obedience of itself has

no moral value or use in the development of the child's personality. It is useful only as a means to some other end. It is generally agreed that some obedience is required in the early years. For example, the child must understand that he may not go into situations that are dangerous to himself, such as near a hot stove and on to a road with motor traffic; but it is desirable to reduce these things to a minimum by devices which prevent the child from going to these places. Some parents will reply. ' This is all very well, but how am I going to get the child to do the things he ought to do unless he is obedient? ' The true answer to this lies again in the parent-child relationship. If there is a friendly co-operative relationship between mother and child, the child will in the main like to do the things the mother wants him to do. If again there is a war on, or competition for mastery, which has originated in the first year, the situation will be the reverse of this and the child negativistic. This situation once established is difficult to retrieve.

A clearer view of these problems can be obtained if the parent will think constantly not only of the present situation and its immediate difficulties but also of the ultimate consequences of her attitude on the behaviour of the child when he becomes adult and away from her charge. It is enormously easier to manage an obedient, submissive and intimidated child, but what will happen when he grows up? There are two main possibilities. One is that he will now kick himself free of the traces and do all the things he feels inclined to do without any consideration for other people—in other words, become irresponsible and undisciplined. The other is that he may always look for authority to tell him whether he should or should not do a certain thing, and suffer from indecision and lack of initiative.

Summing up. then, the real object to be attained is self-discipline, which is achieved best by free co-operation with the parent with a minimum of commands and prohibitions. What is ordinarily known as the ' problem of discipline ' will scarcely arise where such co-operation exists.

21.—PUNISHMENT

THE question of punishment as a whole may perhaps be regarded as more in the domain of the educationalist than of the psychiatrist. The latter, however, can say that, while it may be impossible in practice to avoid it completely, punishment is unfortunate, and from the point of view of later mental health the minimum is desirable: that punishment by deprivation of privilege is to be preferred: and that any punishment that operates by exciting fear is bad. It is on the question of *corporal* punishment that the psychiatrist must speak: this is a matter essentially within his domain: it is not a matter for educationalists to pronounce upon despite their assumption of this prerogative.

' Corporal punishment is dangerous to Mental Health.' This is a statement that can be made unequivocally. It is a statement of the same order as, ' It is dangerous to drink water contaminated with typhoid bacilli.' The earlier in life it is given the more dangerous it is. If psychiatrists, especially psycho-analysts, were to give an account of the number of cases in which corporal punishment in early life was the source of grave personality disorders in adult life, the community would probably be astonished. Both sexes are involved. The danger is greatest where the first year has been unsatisfactory, that is, where the child feels deprived and unloved and therefore harbours some resentment and fear towards the parent. There is a kind of war or competition for mastery: the child is difficult to manage. Corporal punishment at this early stage is commonly administered on the buttocks. We have previously indicated that certain zones or regions of the body are endowed with an intensified capacity for sensuous feelings. One of these zones is the buttocks. This region is sensuously excitable by stimulation in both sexes throughout life but in adult males (as distinct from females) this capacity usually declines in importance. In the young of both sexes the buttocks are highly sensitive, and sensuous or erotic feelings are easily aroused by stimulation. It is essential to note that these feelings may be aroused not only by stimulation which has an affectionate or caressing purpose, but also by blows (whether by hand or instrument) which are intended to cause pain and inflict punishment, and have no such affectionate purpose. As a result of smacking or hitting on the buttocks the child experiences intense sensuous feelings which should normally be associated with a friendly, tender or loving relationship with the other person or parent. In this situation of corporal punishment, then, the child feels that the parent is angry with him (or her) and hates him (at least temporarily); that the parent intends to hurt him. He feels pain, fear, perhaps rage and hate, perhaps guilt as well; but in addition to these feelings he experiences intense sensuous feelings normally associated with a love relationship. If the deprivation has been severe in the first year there may be an intense craving for some sort of personal intimacy involving sensuous gratification by whatever method or in whatever region of the body.

It is possible that the sensuous excitement produced by smacking the buttocks may proceed to orgasm—an experience of itself disturbing to the child. This combination of feelings —fear, pain, hate, guilt and love constitutes an emotional situation which the child is unable to cope with: it is intolerable and can only be dealt with by dissociation and repression. The immediate result of this will be a still more complicated and morbid relationship with the mother: the later result may be a permanent masochistic attitude (probably unconscious) which may amount to a complete masochistic perversion. And this may occur in males as well as females.

Thus smacking a young child of either sex may be an important factor in the production of neurosis. Sometimes the punishment is inflicted on account of some infantile sensuous behaviour, e.g. masturbation, thumbsucking, bedwetting, etc. of which the parent disapproves. In this case, then, the beating excites just those feelings which he has been told are wicked, and the feelings of fear and guilt are correspondingly still more intense and the conflict more acute. Just as masochistic feelings are excited in the child, so sadistic feelings may be operating in the parent. The association of sensuous or erotic feelings (sadistic or masochistic) with thrashing or 'flagellation' is well known and has been exploited in literature. This, however, usually refers to adults: the sources in infancy are not so widely appreciated.

It is commonly asked why there should be such danger in caning adolescent boys for breaking school rules. The answer is that the danger is not excessive provided the punisher knows both his own and his victim's unconscious motives and also knows the whole history of the latter with regard to punishment in infancy! It is quite useless to question the victim about such a matter because all the critical sensuous and guilt-producing experiences will be quite unconscious or 'forgotten.' It must not be supposed that the people who have suffered from beating in childhood are aware of it or come complaining of it. They are quite unaware of it and will frequently say that their parents were good and kind. The associated symptoms are effectively disguised.

But apart from all this, what possible benefit can be derived from corporal punishment? Its object is to produce 'moral' or desired behaviour as a result of pain and fear. Clearly no real morality can be achieved in this way.

It was stated earlier that educationalists *per se* were not entitled to pronounce upon corporal punishment. At a meeting in New Zealand a few years ago, a headmaster advanced the view that corporal punishment must be right because the Bible said so! For the sake of the remainder, I should add that he is not typical of all headmasters in the country. He (the headmaster) was probably referring to the maxim 'Spare the rod and spoil the child' which is apparently derived from the Book of Proverbs. This is usually attributed to King Solomon: but whatever the source, it is probably three thousand years old. Many will think it imprudent and childish to accept without enquiry a statement made by someone so long ago; especially since we have no available evidence to show that the writer was a good parent! But unfortunately there are still people who share this view and a still larger number who consider themselves qualified to express opinions about corporal punishment, though utterly ignorant of the factors and forces involved and oblivious of their own unconscious motives.

The only safe rule about corporal punishment is to follow the safe rule, 'Hit someone of your own size only,'—that is, if you must hit someone. As regards children, this would mean, 'If you must hit your son wait until he is as strong as yourself and then it will not be so dangerous (to him)! Do not hit girls at all.'

22.—FATHERS

IF any fathers have succeeded in reading as far as this, they may be asking where they come into the picture, whether they matter at all, and whether they have any function to play in the drama beyond that of fertilizing agents. It is true, I think, that in the first year, and largely in the second, the father's rôle in direct relationship with the child is much less important than that of the mother. But it is far from the truth to suppose that they do not matter and have no function to perform. In the first place, they must be sufficiently good husbands to cause their wives to look forward to becoming pregnant and producing a child. The next important function is during pregnancy. During this period the woman becomes increasingly dependent upon the husband's support and encouragement. In a primitive community she would need to be especially protected from dangers at this time. In such a community the dangers would be of such an obvious kind as attacks from enemies, animals, fire and flood, from cold or starvation. In a modern community these particular dangers —except in time of war—are presumably absent, but the need for protection is still present.

First of all and obviously she will need to feel economically secure; secondly, perhaps, that he will be at hand at times when she needs him and not away playing golf or billiards, still less consuming alcohol at the neighbouring pub; over and above this, she will need moral support in anticipating and facing what may be to her an ordeal, especially if it is to be her first child.

In order to meet this, it will be necessary for him to become informed to an adequate extent about the nature of the whole process which she is to experience. He will be of no use to her if he takes such a line as ' I do not know anything about these things, this is your affair.' We might venture to add that in some circumstances he may have to protect her against too peremptory doctors and nurses. He can only do this if he has made himself well-informed about the whole process. This need of support becomes more marked as childbirth approaches and is intense at the time of childbirth. It is unfortunate that a convention has developed in which doctors regard husbands as superfluous and even a nuisance during

51

childbirth, and try to keep them out of the way. We have elsewhere advocated conscious (non-narcotized) childbirth and here the close presence and support of the husband is most desirable.

The same conditions apply after birth and continue while the child is young: the father's rôle now is the support (material and moral) of the mother as well as the children, so that both have a sense not only of material security but also of emotional security based upon a feeling of harmony and accord.

As the child gets older, and particularly when he is able to understand language, he will, and should, turn his attention increasingly to the father. This does not imply that previously in the early period the father should stand aloof and keep his hands off the children: he may well assist the mother in dealing with them and in the demonstration of affection. Normally, however, he will here have to play a subordinate rôle to the mother. It is unnecessary here to discuss at length the rôle of the father except to refer to certain important matters. It is most undesirable that the father should seek, or allow to develop, a situation in which he is regarded as the disciplinarian who is called in to administer punishment. It is not uncommon to hear, 'You wait till your father comes home.'

One also hears frequently the father saying that the mother is too soft with the children and they should be 'brought up tough' or 'licked into shape.' This is a false doctrine besides being an unwarranted interference with what is the mother's province. As regards 'bringing them up tough' it is worth mentioning another of the apparent paradoxes which this subject presents. Parents (usually fathers) often suppose that the best way to make their sons courageous is to expose them frequently to frightening situations or to coerce them into enterprises of which they are afraid. This method usually produces the opposite of that desired, that is, it is the way to produce a permanently timid individual. It is the opposite policy—of assurance of protection from danger and the feeling that he will not be asked to do something which he is unsure of, which will conduce to the confident, courageous child. In fairness to the father one might add here that a timid, anxious child may also be produced if the parent (usually the mother) habitually shows anxiety about any enterprise or adventure that the child may conceive. This is an illustration of the principle mentioned elsewhere that neurosis is infectious or contagious—transmitted from parent to offspring in this way and not by heredity. Morbid anxiety in either parent will be caught by the child.

23.—APPLICATION TO CHILDBIRTH AND OBSTETRICS

WE have earlier stressed the vital importance of good parenthood, especially good motherhood in the first year of life, and have explained that it is essential for the parent to be emotionally mature. It is important, therefore, to discuss the conditions which promote or retard the development of emotional maturity. We have referred to some of these earlier, but now wish to propound the view that the act and function of childbirth is an important factor in this development, and also that, in order to produce its full effect, the childbirth must be a conscious process in the mother—or perhaps better expressed—that the mother should be conscious at the actual birth of the child and also immediately afterwards. It is commonly observed that in most women there is a change of personality toward maturity after childbirth, whether she is conscious or narcotized during the process. In biological terms, this would be called the stimulation of a previously latent maternal instinct. The endocrinologists tell us that changes take place in the endocrine glands (notably the pituitary) during the process of childbirth. And some may contend that this is independent of consciousness. We readily accept the physiology of these changes, but we think that psychologically speaking the process of maturation is incomplete if the mother is narcotized during the process. Anything in the nature of scientific proof of the statement would be difficult to provide, but the best evidence comes from the women themselves. We discuss this question elsewhere and so do not propose now to do so at length; but it would be difficult to deny that the conscious act of producing a living child must be the crowning experience in the fulfilment of womanhood; and this view is supported by spontaneous expressions of women themselves. It must be admitted, however, that if a woman has not reached a certain level of maturity, and therefore looks forward rather with dread than with joyful expectation to motherhood, this feeling is not apparent. We contend, therefore, that while the conscious experience of childbirth is not the only factor in producing emotional maturity, it is an essential and culminating one. Apart from this, we have maintained that for the future mother-child relationship it is vitally important that the mother should be conscious at the time of birth and also aware of the child as a person immediately afterwards.

There is a little carol (*A Cradle Song of the Blessed Virgin*) which runs:

> O Lamb, my love inviting,
> O Star, my soul delighting,
> O Flower of mine own bearing,
> O Jewel past comparing!
>
> My child of might indwelling,
> My sweet, all sweets excelling,
> Of bliss the fountain flowing,
> The dayspring ever glowing!
>
> My Joy, my exultation,
> My spirit's consolation;
> My son, my spouse, my brother,
> O listen to thy Mother.

It is difficult to suppose that the ecstasy suggested in these verses could be experienced fully by a mother who has been narcotized during the process of childbirth. She must then regain consciousness at some time after the delivery and discover that the child is born: to some extent it must be an act of faith on her part to accept the assurance that the baby presented to her is her child.

24.—APPLICATION TO GENERAL MEDICINE

UNTIL comparatively recently the diseases of men were supposed to be of two types:

1. Diseases of the body, the signs of which could be objectively or mechanically observed, and having some kind of physical causation.

2. Diseases of the mind. the source of which was much more obscure.

It was assumed that these two types of diseases were distinct from one another.

At a later period, on account of the advances in physical medicine, it was assumed that diseases of the mind were also due to disturbances or abnormalities of the body, and this developed the department known as neuro-psychiatry. It is of course true that some diseases of the mind, e.g. Cretinism, Korsakow's psychosis and dementia paralytica are due to bodily conditions, but the discovery of analytical psychology in proving that emotional conflict in childhood can produce mental disorder, and the fact that this type of disorder can be cured by a specific form of mental treatment, has led to new conceptions—the latest stage in this process of change in attitude to disease is the invention of the term ' psycho-somatic disorders.' ' Psychosomatic ' is Greek for ' mind-body.' Its emergence was due to the discovery that some recognizable diseases involving organs of the body occurred in persons who at the same time suffered from neurosis or emotional disorder. It was also observed that the emotional disorder appeared to play a part in the production of the disease, and further, that the cure of the emotional disorder led to relief of the physical disorder unless irreversible bodily changes had taken place. It had been previously observed that in cases of frank conversion hysteria (where the physical symptoms are symbolic or represent an idea) there were physical symptoms. The term ' psycho-somatic disorders ' has been used to include a category much wider than that of conversion hysteria alone. This, then, is a very notable change in the medical outlook, and in so far as the term ' psycho-somatic ' is accepted by orthodox medicine, it means first the concession of the principle that so-called organic (physical) disease may be produced by emotional (mental) processes as essential causes. But the term ' psycho-somatic disorders ' is open to the criticism that there are not only two but three types of diseases: (1) physical, (2) mental, (3) psycho-somatic.

Now since man is a creature with two apparent components, mind and body, which are inseparable in function, it must be true that all his diseases are in fact psycho-somatic. This term will apply to the disease of a broken leg on the one hand and obsessional neurosis on the other: though no doubt the effective treatment of the first will be physical, and of the other, psychic. And this will hold, whatever metaphysical view be held as to the ultimate reality—mind or matter—monism or dualism.

In this connection I should like to quote the wise words of Dr. Edward Weiss:

' Psycho-somatic medicine is an approach to medicine that applies to all aspects of medicine and surgery . . . it does not mean to study the soma less; it only means to study the psyche more. World War I established psychiatry on a firm, scientific basis, and World War II is seeing its final integration into general medicine. When that integration is complete, we will no longer need the term " psycho-somatic " because all good medicine will be psycho-somatic.'*

It has been tragic for medicine that the study of the psyche was omitted from it. Another term that is simpler and more expressive than ' psycho-somatic medicine ' is *human medicine*; and I should like to commend *The Human Approach* by Henry Yellowlees (London: J. and A. Churchill Ltd., 1946). There is much in this book with which I profoundly agree. For example, he is concerned to dispose of the fallacious idea that there are such things as diseases, i.e. entities which vaguely exist somewhere and descend upon people out of the blue. This doctrine has of course acquired great strength as a result of the discovery of bacteria, and it is true that some diseases are in part a result of the invasion of the organism by bacteria, but even here there is not only the question of the bacteria but also the question of immunity to be considered. Actually the only real entity is a *sick person*. To say that so-and-so has ' got ' pneumonia or phthisis, or fibrositis, is loose and unscientific talk. These terms are useful labels to indicate the ways in which people get ill, but it is to be borne in mind that what must be treated is not the thing called pneumonia but a person who is ill in a way that is convenient to describe by this term. If one treats a person in this way one is less likely to miss the essential psychic factors than if one conceives the phenomenon

* ' Psycho-therapy in Everyday Practice' in *Modern Attitudes in Psychiatry*, Edward Weiss, M.D.; Columbia University Press, 1946.

as a matter purely of lungs and pneumococci. The question can 'still be asked why this particular person's lungs were invaded by pneumococci at this particular time. I have only selected one matter for comment out of Dr. Yellowlees' book, but it is full of material highly relevant to our theme.

If Dr. Weiss is right in his statement that all good medicine will be psycho-somatic (and I for one emphatically agree with him), then we can surely change the tense and say that all good medicine *is* psycho-somatic. We can then presumably infer that medicine that is not psycho-somatic is not good: and it cannot be denied that in the last few generations the vast bulk of medical practice has not been psycho-somatic. Such reflections surely must give us furiously to think. Many physicians pay lip service to the idea that man has a ' psyche,' but their method of treatment shows that they have no real belief in its existence or in its capacity to affect the organism as a whole. Some would deny this and insist that they believe in the psyche and its power to affect the organism, but are at a loss to know how to deal with this situation. This means that they do not know how to cope with problems of personal relationship—with other people's feelings in relation to their own.

If, then, it is true that much of the approach to human disease by physicians at present is limited and inadequate. how have we gotten into this situation? I think that there are two broad answers to this question: and they are inter-related. One is that medicine, being partly scientific, is based upon metaphysical conceptions as to the nature of reality which were dominant in the preceding generation. The dominant conception a generation ago was mechanistic and materialistic: it seemed that physics and chemistry would be able to explain everything, including life and thought. We are just now emerging from this state, and the production of the term ' psycho-somatic ' is an indication of this. The other factor is that we as a community are primitive in our own personal relationships. i.e. emotionally immature. We are afraid of our own and of other persons' feelings, and this involves doctors as well as everyone else. There is no doubt that many doctors are afraid of investigating personal feelings; many others also are disinclined to devote the time necessary to such a procedure. There is no doubt that expenditure of time is required.

Returning, however, to our theme, the relevance of the term 'psycho-somatic' to our present purpose is that some at least frank 'organic' disease may be due to neurosis and thus due to disturbances of early nurture. The best approach to these diseases (which present the appearance of being organic in nature) is by education in mental hygiene and hence prophylaxis and prevention. The second best is to deal with the mental and emotional factors involved when the disease is first seen and thus arrest the morbid process as far as possible.

25.—MARRIAGE

SINCE our central purpose is to stress the importance of motherhood, and more particularly good motherhood, we must consider problems of marriage. To discuss this complicated problem adequately would require a book in itself and we will refer only to those matters which are closely relevant to our theme. It is often suggested that persons proposing to marry should obtain beforehand a medical certificate of fitness. This certificate is usually assumed to refer to physical health except that frank insanity (severe psychosis) will usually be considered. Very little attention has been paid to psychological fitness for marriage. We have employed the phrase 'emotional maturity' and sought to give some explanations of its meaning. Marriage presumes parenthood; and if it is necessary for people to be emotionally mature in order to be good parents it follows that they should also have reached a reasonable degree of emotional maturity before marriage. A person may be physically fit and may be quite capable of reproduction in the biological sense and yet quite unfit for parenthood or even marriage in the psychological sense, because emotionally immature. He or she may be quite capable of the reproduction of healthy offspring but quite unfitted for healthy nurture of such offspring or perhaps to sustain a harmonious marriage. It is very unlikely that any government would be prepared to rule that certificated emotional maturity should be a condition for marriage; and such legislation would do nothing to relieve the problem of illegitimacy which is already serious enough. But it is very desirable that persons about to marry should be encouraged to submit themselves to an examination in respect of their psychic adaptation to marriage and parenthood. This would be to their own advantage. It would also have the effect of reducing the number of broken marriages. The broken marriage is well known as a potent cause of personality disorder in children, and we have omitted reference to it not because it is unimportant but because it is well recognized.

Regarding preparation for marriage, much is heard about the wise selection of a mate. It is often assumed that if care is exercised a correct choice can be made and a happy marriage follow. It is not sufficiently recognized that many people who are physically fit and biologically marriageable are not psychologically mature enough for a satisfactory marriage with anyone; and therefore it is very misleading to suppose that if they exercise enough care they will make a right choice. Actually in this situation whatever choice they make will be a wrong one. It would be more helpful to suggest that they undertake some treatment towards the attainment of a degree of emotional maturity which would fit them for a conjugal adjustment. The words ' right ' and ' wrong ' may possibly seem obscure here: they are not used in any moral sense. By a right choice we imply that it will lead to a satisfactory and happy marriage and parenthood; a wrong one is the opposite of this. There may be some who will query this rather sweeping generalization and state that they have observed marriages which appear to be satisfactory and happy where one of the parties is obviously emotionally immature. It is worthwhile to consider this objection. It is true that a young man who is very dependent upon his mother and perhaps has infantile attitudes towards her may marry a very maternal woman with a resulting marriage that is apparently in a happy equilibrium. Correspondingly a young woman who is obviously immature may marry a man who has strong paternal feelings. Here again. apparent equilibrium may result. In these situations, however, I think the criterion is not this apparent equilibrium but what happens to the children of such marriages. In many cases the children will suffer some disability in their emotional development because of the emotional immaturity of one of

the parents, and the consequent departure from an ideal conjugal combination. Therefore in considering the principle,
we must see the final result in the emotional development of
the offspring. On the other hand, we do not wish to exaggerate
the importance of this. Most authorities would agree that
although such marriages are not ideal, the apparent harmony
that exists between the parents is far more favourable to the
children than cases where there is hate and discord.

26.—' SEX EDUCATION '

THE phrase ' sex education ' is much in vogue in these days.
There is much searching and questioning as to who should
give it, where it should be given and when. Actually it would
be better if the phrase were abolished, as it has no clear
meaning and its use leads to a great deal of confusion. It
may be used to refer to instruction in the anatomy and
physiology of the human reproductive organs; or it may
refer to instruction in the development of reproductive function in the evolutionary sense from lower forms; or it may
refer to teaching of morals regarding so-called sexual
behaviour. Many well-intentioned people are concerned at
the chaotic state that exists in our culture in the sphere of
marriage, divorce, illegitimacy, perversions, etc. They observe
in a large number of people who get into great trouble with
marital problems a serious ignorance concerning the facts of
reproduction. They then assume that the troubles they
observe are due to the ignorance, and that these faults will
be corrected by supplying the requisite information. Actually
the inference is a false one. Both the factual ignorance and
the failure of adjustment are due to the same cause, which
is an emotional disturbance. This results in emotional immaturity, or perhaps in neurosis, and has its source in early
childhood.

The real problem which these people are trying to solve
is the problem of personal relationship—in this case the
problem of the relationship between persons of different
sexes. The capacity to solve this problem healthily and
happily depends upon emotions and feelings, much more than
upon the intellect, information and knowledge. It involves

the question of emotional maturity or immaturity and the capacity to love objectively which we have referred to earlier. These feelings and emotions have been developing favourably or unfavourably from the earliest years of the child's life, before reason or intellect in the adult sense becomes operative. The emotional trends and habits established in those early years are little influenced by the development of reason. Whereas for a healthy solution of the problem a capacity to love objectively is required, so in the morbid conditions which unfortunately are so common, the two pathological emotions of fear and guilt tend to dominate the picture in regard to all personal relationships other than superficial ones. These emotions of fear and guilt are in antithesis to love and prevent its satisfactory development. The same emotions (of fear and guilt) also may apply to any interest in the problem of conjugal relationship or knowledge about it.

I said earlier that it would be better if the phrase ' sex education ' were abolished. The dictionary meaning given to the word ' sex ' is ' being male or female or hermaphrodite.' It is difficult to see how to proceed with education in that. This is no mere quibble: an important principle is involved. The existence of the phrase ' sex education ' itself is an indication of a confusion in thought, and, still more important, a confusion in feeling and emotion. The real problem here is that of relationship between persons and, therefore, the appropriate label is ' education in personal relationship.' More precisely, the problem is the problem of love relationship, and the task involved is education in *love*. Viewed thus, in its true light, the problem may seem more formidable. How are you to educate people in their love feelings? But the fact that the phrase ' sex education ' is used so widely is an indication of the slough and confusion in which our culture is involved. It represents an attempt to divorce ' sex ' or ' sex feeling ' from love; this has, in appearance, been partly successful and the results have been disastrous.

Many people to-day, both thoughtful and otherwise, are perplexed about the problem as well as emotionally confused, and there is no simple solution. We are in a state of flux about it and must continue so for some time. It will only be solved by a true education in love and this must begin in infancy if at all. It is not an intellectual matter.

It will be observed that education in love is largely the same problem as the production of mental health. The word 'love' has been used on several occasions above; and it is necessary to indicate the meaning attached to it. For assuredly in our language it is called upon to carry a heavy burden of diverse meanings. It is used here to mean a capacity for a type of relationship with another person. This relationship is essentially mutual or reciprocal though not necessarily co-equal; and it is a complete relationship involving the whole person, i.e. all the component parts of each person are involved. It is also, in essence, a primitive or fundamental relationship, and therefore the emotional and conative components will be relatively more potent than the intellectual, though this component will have its proper place.

It must be added that if one is to begin to understand love one must consider how it originates and develops, and also what it may become. It is found that this capacity for love begins in early infancy in a primitive embryonic form; and that under favourable nurture it develops with the growth of the personality. If, on the other hand, this favourable nurture is absent (i.e. if the child is not adequately loved), it may never develop beyond a very primitive form throughout the life of the person. It follows that if one concedes the existence of love feelings, or a capacity for love, in the infant, as one must, this love or capacity is a very different thing from that of a mentally healthy mature adult; though the former is the essential germ or nucleus of the latter. Education in love then must begin in infancy; if this early education (nurture) is missed it can only be retrieved with the greatest difficulty. Evidently this essential beginning is the concern of the parents rather than of the school. But the process begun by the parents must in later childhood be implemented and fostered by a wider environment and notably by the school.

What, then, can be done about this problem? First seek by every means to ensure that the first year of life is healthy and that a really satisfactory mother-child relationship develops. If this has not been achieved and the fact is realized. seek the best therapeutic help that can be obtained for both mother and child to retrieve the situation.

It is true that the essential facts of reproduction should be known and understood before the age of puberty in both sexes. But this should be part of a well-assimilated system of knowledge resulting from a gradual development from early childhood, and related to corresponding knowledge of animal and vegetable life. Under healthy conditions it will so develop quite naturally as a result of frank but suitable answers to children's questions. It is therefore the responsibility of the parents; and they may not transfer the responsibility to the schools. If they feel themselves incapable of carrying out the task they are inadequate as parents and should seek therapeutic help for the emotional disorder from which they suffer.

As regards factual information—under healthy conditions, the child begins to ask questions about birth and reproduction about the third year. If he does not, there is cause for concern, for something in the mother-child relationship is standing in the way. Under normal conditions he will by stages ask more advanced questions, all of which should be answered truthfully and with due regard for the comprehension of the child.

In our culture with its artificiality and separation from the natural world, it is highly desirable that in every school, from the infant department onwards, there should be instruction given in simple biology, including the evolution of methods of reproduction. This will lead on to the scientific approach to reproduction in man and put the latter in its true perspective. A biologist has recently asked the very pertinent question: ' How can a man call himself educated who knows nothing about the world of living things or his place in relation to it? '

It is to be noted that there is something wrong in the situation when adolescents have to be informed about the simplest facts of human reproduction, i.e. about the processes by which they themselves came into existence. Part of the explanation is that such information is withheld from them, in town dwellers especially, by a conspiracy of silence. There is such confusion of mind about the matter and so much perfusion with feelings of guilt that parents shrink from tackling the problem. It is most fallacious that this emotional problem can be solved by supplying the necessary information. If the parents are really adequate no problem of explicit ' sex education ' arises.

27.—'SEXUAL' ABERRATIONS

I HAVE avoided the term 'perversion' to avoid a rather technical discussion of what is and is not a perversion. A perversion may be defined as a mode of expression of the reproductive instinct which precludes its normal biological fulfilment, that is, reproduction. To discuss these fully would be too technical and also inappropriate here. But it is relevant to refer to masturbation and to homosexuality.

Masturbation

So much has been written and said recently about masturbation in refutation of the shocking nonsense that was said and believed a generation ago, that the subject has become a little hackneyed. It should be noted that masturbation is a symptom, not a disease; it is very common and in a great majority of cases is of trivial importance; but sometimes it is a symptom of severe mental conflict. This conflict is important not because of the masturbation but because of the social and psychological effects of the guilt feelings with which it is associated. In such disturbing conflicts the source of the trouble is in the first year: deprivation and frustration of satisfaction at the breast compel the child to seek compensation in the only way remaining to him, that is, in his own person. This may take the form of masturbation or thumb sucking which are broadly equivalent. Frequently this form of masturbation is punished or threatened in its turn, and thus a conflict is established which becomes fixed. It may remain latent through the later years of childhood and reappear in early adolescence; its original source has by then been lost sight of.

Homosexuality

The problem of homosexuality is still one about which psychiatrists are not all agreed. Therefore opinions regarding it must be expressed with some hesitation. I think, however, that it is appropriate to express briefly my own opinion about it here. I think that there are frequently innate, temperamental factors which enter into its production; but I do not think that these are the determining factors. As regards homosexuality in males, my own psychiatric experiences have provided very strong evidence that the essential factor is the total failure to establish a sensuous love relationship with the mother in the first year: the individual then is compelled to seek satisfaction either in auto-erotic (masturbatory) activities or by homosexual activities, or by both. The homosexual activities as a rule do not appear until later childhood and it seems probable that the attitude may be precipitated fortuitously by meeting a person of similar proclivities. It is therefore amenable to treatment by psychotherapy provided the individual is dissatisfied with his condition. It is therefore also most unjust to treat these people as morally degraded. Such an attitude intensifies their disability.

The essential elements here, and those most relevant to our main theme are:

1. That homosexuality is a problem of personal relationship.

2. That the essential cause is the failure to establish a sensuous or love relationship with the mother in the first year, and that therefore all subsequent women are excluded from this relationship.

3. That as a perversion it is preventible, and also, if taken early, curable, provided the individual has enough patience and fortitude to stay the course of treatment. which is long and arduous.

It should be noted that everyone of both sexes normally passes through a homosexual phase in the course of development. This phase occurs in early adolescence.

Therefore homosexuality if it persists as a perversion into adult life is always a sign of emotional immaturity.

Homosexuality in women, while very common, is in my experience a less profound disposition as a rule, than that occurring in men. In women also I think the fundamental determining experiences occur in the first year.

28.—APPLICATION TO EDUCATION

IT has been pointed out by many people that the critical state of the world at present is largely to be explained by the fact that men have discovered and made for themselves very potent and dangerous machines but have not reached a standard of development in wisdom necessary for the adequate control and use of such instruments. We have elsewhere referred to this by saying that man has made enormous strides in the intellectual and scientific field but no corresponding advance in emotional development: that in the capacity to live a truly human life in societies and families man has progressed very little in the last one thousand years: that he is intellectually precocious and emotionally immature. It would seem that this represents a problem for education as well as for medicine. At present the trend of education seems to be more in the direction of technical training and instruction than in personal development. It would seem necessary to pay much greater attention to emotional or personal education than at present.

We have sought to indicate that the main elements of personality whether good or bad, healthy or morbid, are established by the age of five. School education usually begins about this period. It would seem, therefore, that directors of education should turn their attention to these first five years: this is the period in which the foundations are laid and the concrete set upon which all subsequent education must be constructed: and it is very difficult to alter these foundations once the building has begun.

Nevertheless, emotional development does not cease at the age of five, and it must be in fact the function of teachers to influence its further development. This will call for very high personal qualities in teachers, qualities of which high academic honours and degrees give very little indication. For example, teachers may accentuate emotional conflicts begun in infancy, as a result of which symptoms may appear when the children go to school, such as enuresis, stammering, night terrors, etc. For this the teacher or the school may be blamed, though it should only bear a minor portion of responsibility. So also a good teacher may mitigate these conflicts if he or she has these high personal qualities which will correspond to emotional maturity. But we wish again to emphasize that the labours of these teachers will be of little avail or at least will be greatly hampered if the nurture of the first five years has been inadequate. It will be obvious that the teacher is a parent-substitute and the child's attitude to the teacher will be a reflection of the attitude to the parent, whether this be one of fear and hate on the one hand or of friendliness and confidence on the other. This means that different children will interpret the gestures and tone of the teacher in very different ways.

Our practical conclusion is that personality education begins in the first year of life and that therefore it is the task of the parents. It should therefore be the responsibility of educational authorities to see by every means available that parents are fitted for their task.

29.—STAMMERING AND ITS PSYCHO-PATHOLOGY*

(Reprinted from the Journal of the Christchurch Psychological Society.)

THE speech therapist has to deal with cases of speech defect which vary in nature and origin. For our present purpose we can divide them into two large groups; one where the speech defect is the result of organic disturbance or defect in the speech organs, or in that department of the central nervous system that controls them; the other where there is no discoverable defect in the speech organs or any discoverable disease or disturbance in the central nervous system. This second group will be equivalent to all those forms of speech defect which are included in stammering or stuttering. It is with this latter group that the medical psychologist is chiefly concerned. Stammering or stuttering occurring in young children may be temporary and due to various transient influences; but when it persists into later childhood, i.e., from the age of seven or eight onwards, it is a symptom of psychoneurosis or allied emotional disturbance. Correspondingly, then, the treatment of it is a branch of psychotherapy, and all the principles that apply to psychotherapy in general, apply to the treatment of stammering. It is therefore desirable to enumerate some of these principles.

1. That a psychoneurosis is a disorder of the emotional life, or what means the same thing, an interference with the capacity of the individual to adjust himself to other people.

* This paper was read in the Special Speech Therapy Division of the Social Science Section of the Science Congress of the Royal Society held in Wellington, May, 1947.

2. That the source and origin of a psychoneurosis will always be found in early childhood—certainly within the first five years and usually within the first three.

3. That a psychoneurosis will be produced largely by the pathological operation of the emotions of fear and guilt.

4. That these emotions may or may not be conscious to the patient and are frequently wholly, or in part, unconscious.

5. That these pathogenic emotions of fear and guilt represent one side of an endo-psychic conflict; the other side of the conflict being taken by some natural spontaneous or instinctive tendency in the individual.

6. That the disorder is produced by some form of inadequate or faulty nurture on the part of the parents. or of those who have had charge of the individual in infancy.

We have noted earlier that stammering, being a symptom of a psycho-neurosis. therefore had its origins in infancy or early childhood. As a symptom then stammering or stuttering is of peculiar interest. The sounds of which the speech is composed issue from the mouth of the individual. Articulate speech is only one of the functions of the nose and throat; from the phylogenetic point of view it is a function that has developed very late. being present only in *Homo-sapiens.* In any individual also, it is not a primary function—the first and primary function of the mouth is that of sucking or chewing or corresponding activities, which subserve nutrition. As has been rightly pointed out (by Blanton and Blanton for example) under certain abnormal emotional conditions in the individual. the secondary function, i.e.. speech, may fail to develop adequately, because the organs concerned have the tendency to revert to the primary function; i.e.. chewing or sucking; though it would be better to say that the person as a whole has a tendency in this direction, rather than say that the organs themselves have any wishes. The result then is that when the stammerer essays to speak, the movements of the primary function tend to overwhelm those of the secondary. As soon as he attempts to utter words, movements intrude which correspond wholly or partly to sucking or blowing. chewing, vomiting, swallowing or biting. These movements interfere with or completely overwhelm the movements necessary to clear and free speech. There will often be added strenuous attempts to check or control these involuntary movements—attempts which are usually unsuccessful and increase the general spasm. This voluntary effort to control the primitive movements will occur more with the individual of the anxiety type than with the hysterical type. the former being more self-conscious than the latter.

Looking at the matter then in its crudest form, in the earliest phase of development, food in the form of milk goes into the mouth, and something more than this—intimate contact via the mouth with another person; this represents the primary function. In the secondary function air in the form of sound vibrations goes out. Physically they are air vibrations. *psychically* they are words and ideas. Furthermore in both functions there is communication with another person. We do not normally speak into empty space. Sometimes we do thus speak, thinking there is another person present. When we discover that we are alone the sound of our own speech has a peculiar emotional effect upon us, as if it were coming back to us instead of passing across to another person; so that both in breast-feeding and in speech—both in the primary and secondary functions of these organs—there is normally a communication with another person or persons. In normal speech our ideas flow out in a more or less steady, rhythmic, continuous stream to some person who is assumed to be listening; in stammering that does not happen. The sound and the air current are checked or blocked or inhibited or confused; rhythm is absent. The sounds and the air current are checked because they tend to convey certain feelings and ideas. Earlier we said that under some abnormal conditions the organs involved in speech (the lips, tongue, palate, mouth, pharynx, etc.) tend to revert to their primary function. What, then are these conditions? There is evidence to indicate that if the infant has not been able to establish a satisfactory relationship that will involve complete reciprocity, freedom, spontaneity, harmony and rhythm in the primary function (nutrition and breast-feeding) it will not be able, when it comes to the secondary function, to develop fluent speech, which depends upon a relationship, or a capacity for a relationship, to another person which involves just these features. In terms of emotion, if the infant has not been able to establish a satisfactory relationship to the mother in the breast-feeding situation. it will become the victim of emotional

conflict, which will involve the excitation of the emotions of
fear and guilt in relation to its mother; and as the mother is
the prototype of all subsequent relationships, afterwards with
other people as well. We can say, then, that when the
stammerer essays to speak to another person, he will be
affected by emotions of fear and guilt, or both, towards this
person, though he may be unconscious of both emotions; and
it is these emotions which block or frustrate or inhibit the
free spontaneous flow of speech. What is being inhibited,
however, is not in the first case the speech or words, but the
feelings towards the other person, of which the speech is the
'vehicle.' The actual interference with the sounds and movements by these emotions corresponds to the emotional conflict.
Observation of people who speak well, or those whose speech
is pleasant to listen to, independently of the thought content
of it, will suggest that these people enjoy making sounds or
words. One of the first essentials in breast-feeding is the
experience of mutual and reciprocal enjoyment. Certainly
the stammerer is unable to enjoy speaking to another person
—that is to say, when he is in fact stammering; but it is well
known that stammerers are frequently able to speak freely to
certain people and not to others. Perhaps it is that the
stammerer may not or dare not enjoy speaking to certain
persons. This pervasion with fear of the stammerer is fairly
obvious in his general demeanour—at any rate, in those who
belong to the anxiety type. It will be less apparent (apart
from the stammer) in the cases of hysteria, where the stammering may be regarded as a conversion symptom and fear and
anxiety are completely unconscious and are not observable
as such.

We have offered two suggestions as to the mechanism or
explanation of stammering; (1) That it is due to the paralysing influence of the emotions of fear and guilt. (2) That
under certain conditions the primary functions of the speech
organs tend to emerge and overwhelm the secondary functions.
But these two are not alternatives; investigation will show
that they are interrelated.

If the secondary function (of speech) is unable to retain
its dominance over the primary function, it might seem that
either the secondary function in its nervous control is relatively weak, or the urge of the primary function must be

relatively strong. An important fact here is that many stammerers can speak normally to certain people. There is no evidence of 'weakness' or lack of control. The real situation is relationship between two persons—the stammerer and the listener. This is an emotional relationship. With certain people the emotions of fear and guilt will be excited and with others they will not. In the latter situation normal speech will be possible. In the former case not only guilt and fear are aroused, but also the whole conflict involving the desires, needs and urges of the primitive infantile situation —these desires and needs are immensely strong.

We must now consider the bearing of these matters upon the question of the treatment of the stammerer. Again, all those principles which apply in general to the treatment of psycho-neurosis will apply, that is, that the personality of the physician or therapist is of paramount importance—more important than an extensive knowledge of the technique of psychotherapy. If it be asked what characteristics of personality are necessary here, the answer will be indicated in the manner of origin of these conditions. If they are brought about by unsatisfactory or inadequate nurture and parenthood, then the therapist will have to provide these conditions which were lacking in the actual parents. He will therefore have to be capable of being a good parent. It is necessary for an adequate parent to have an intelligent and sympathetic understanding for each individual child. This leads us to the second requirement of the therapist, namely, an intelligent and *sympathetic* understanding of his patient. This will necessitate some understanding of common psychopathological mechanisms, and types of situations in which these have their origin. It will be necessary for the therapist to create such an atmosphere that the patient will have confidence or trust in him as a person—an atmosphere in which these morbid emotions of fear and guilt are mitigated directly as far as possible. It is therefore necessary for the therapist to be an adult in the sense of being emotionally mature, and it is also desirable that he should have had as wide an experience of life as possible.

The question of the form of treatment will depend very much upon the age of the patient. The statement made above that stammering is related to experiences in the first year of life suggests that systematic analytical treatment is desirable. This is probably true in the case of many adult stammerers if a radical cure is to be sought. But such systematic analytical treatment is quite unsuited to young children. Less formal and less verbal methods will be necessary. This, however, does not imply that with children the qualities recommended for the therapist do not apply. Even though the method adopted differs widely from what would be called an analytical method, it is most desirable for the therapist to have in his mind ideas of the possible or probable types of experience that his patient has had.

It is the lot of many stammerers to have attention constantly drawn to their speech by their relatives and friends. The motive of these relatives and friends is sometimes unfortunately malicious, but quite frequently the motive is an earnest desire to cure the condition by such attention. We have agreed that stammering is a symptom and not a disease; and therefore the principle applies that it is the disease that must be treated and not the symptom. Speech therapists will be well aware of this principle, namely, that the focussing of attention upon the speech will aggravate the trouble, that is the symptom, and that they must as far as possible attend to everything else about the patient apart from the stammer.

The only real solution lies in prophylaxis and prevention, by the education of the parents and intending parents in the principle of child nurture, and especially mothers in the art of satisfactory breast-feeding. These principles have emerged very largely as the result of the successful treatment of psychoneurosis. Speech therapists have the opportunity and privilege of discovering and verifying principles of mental hygiene from their experiences with patients, and therefore, of spreading the gospel of mental hygiene among the community. This gospel can be reduced to five words—if these be well understood . . . '*The child must be loved.*'

30.—DELINQUENCY

IN many communities there is a movement away from the earlier attitude towards delinquency which regarded the delinquent as just bad and as committing offences against society on a basis of free choice or malice prepense. This attitude is both unintelligent and inhuman. With the existence of unconscious motives firmly established, it is no longer permissible to judge conduct on the assumption of moral responsibility provided the person is not insane in the legal meaning of the word. More than a generation has passed since Samuel Butler in *Erewhon* described a community in which bodily illness was regarded as criminal and was treated by incarceration or other penalty, while criminals and delinquents were treated in hospitals as sick persons. Nowadays. few psychiatrists would hold that all delinquency was the result of sickness, that is, that the criminal or delinquent act was unconsciously determined in every case and that the delinquent had no free choice in the matter. They would regard such a view as extravagant. Most, however, would agree that all delinquents. child or adult, should have a psychiatric examination before sentence or treatment. A certain proportion of crimes are committed as a result of an actual psycho-neurosis where the determinants of the conduct are entirely unconscious and where the individual concerned therefore can have no control.

But apart from specific crimes, there are general attitudes to society of the rebellious. militant, revengeful type which are engendered very early and of which the sources are unknown to the subject concerned. In both these cases the determining experiences have occurred in the first two years. Earlier we spoke of a war or competition for mastery between mother and child in the first year. These general attitudes of hostility to society represent an extension of this war from the parent to adult society as a whole.

In the *Lesson of Okinawa* previously quoted, reference is made and importance attached to the relative absence of crime and delinquency. This absence, like the absence of neurosis, is attributed to good motherhood, and the inference is probably a fair one. The question is whether the inference would apply with equal cogency to such large and heterogeneous communities as exist in the United States. The psychiatrist is not prepared to say that all crime is illness, and therefore treatable by psychological methods. What is important here is that he does insist that some crime is illness. that this illness has its origin in early nurture. that it is preventible. and failing prevention. is amenable to skilled treatment. 73

31.—NEUROSIS AND RELIGION

IT might seem presumptuous in a section of a small book of this kind to attempt to deal with any question involving religion. We must hasten to explain, therefore, what our intention is. First of all, we must be clear about this word ' religion.' It is one of many words with a very vague meaning. It is commonly used to refer to the doctrine of a particular religion; as, for example, one speaks of the Christian or Protestant or the Roman Catholic or the Mohammedan or Hindu religion. Clearly these systems differ rather profoundly from one another, so in that sense there can be religions (in the plural). On the other hand, the word ' religion ' could be used in a much broader and more abstract sense. It would then refer to a man's whole attitude to the universe, to his fellow men, to himself, his attitude to the good, the beautiful, the true. In other words, it would refer to the motives that drive him, the ideals that inspire him, the things that he values most. All these things may be very different from any stated or professed creed that he professes to adhere to. This matter of religion in the abstract is of supreme importance in the development of personality and of mental health, but beyond stating this, we do not intend to discuss the theme further at the moment. We are concerned with the word in its former meaning, i.e., religions, and therefore perhaps the heading should have been ' Neurosis and Religions,' and even in that limited sense we shall only be concerned with certain religions which are classified as Christian.

Let us consider again the nature of these disorders to which the names psychosis, neurosis, and psychoneurosis have been given. If an adult person is afraid of the dark, or closed spaces, afraid of going away from home; or if she or he has a paralysis, a chronic dyspepsia, a chronic headache or backache, for none of which any bodily cause can be found; if he or she is chronically or intermittently depressed or exhausted or sleepless, and again no physical cause exists, what is the real nature of the disorder or illness?

Investigation of these conditions shows that they are disorders of the person as a whole, of the self, the psyche or the soul. These people are all sick in soul. Now, in many churches classified as Christian, the care of souls has been regarded as the prime function of priests or ministers of religion. In our own generation we are witnessing a rapid change in this matter. These persons who are sick in soul are now applying in increasing numbers to physicians and psychiatrists for help, and not to priests and ministers of religion. This surely is a most significant fact. Moreover, among these applying for such help to psychiatrists are to be found a proportion of priests and ministers of religion. Now follows another significant fact: physicians and psychiatrists on investigating these disorders find that in a large proportion of cases, though not in all, their patients are what is commonly called very religious, or in other words, they have been heavily indoctrinated with religious teaching in childhood or youth. It is often impossible to relieve or cure these people, without at least modifying some of these ' religious ' doctrines or beliefs. We have referred earlier to the effects of the doctrine of original sin on the nurture of children by parents who are imbued with this doctrine. We are not concerned here with any given interpretation of this phrase by any theological authority; we are concerned only with the effects of the doctrine upon millions of ordinary men and women. All these doctrines and beliefs have one common effect upon the persons involved. i.e., to imbue them with permanent feelings of fear and guilt in relation to their thought, their feeling and their conduct. As we have mentioned before, these emotions of fear and guilt are very important factors in the production of mental disorders. We are not suggesting that all fear and guilt in the mind is derived directly from religious indoctrination. but a great deal of it is so derived and more is reinforced by it. It seems, therefore, that some teaching that is called religious is inimical to mental health. It will be seen here that what is causing the trouble is ' moral teaching or train-ing ' in the guise of religion. We have referred to the baneful effects of ' moral training ' earlier. It is the inculcation of a morality based upon fear of punishment. It is largely nega-tive and a great deal of it when expressed in words begins with the phrase, ' Thou shalt not.'

So disturbed have psychiatrists become at the magnitude of this problem, that many of them consequently have come to the conclusion that all religion is bad and that mankind in general would improve if it were removed altogether. Here it should be understood, however, that they are thinking in terms of religions and their doctrines rather than religion in the abstract. We are concerned here to report what we discover and we must be careful not to embark upon theological controversy. We cannot, however, avoid the question that arises out of the situation we have been describing. We have referred to the effect of the teaching of religious doctrines by certain churches classified as Christian. Obviously the question arises, ' Is the Christian religion or Christianity, as such, inimical to mental health? ' If the doctrines referred to which involve the feelings of guilt and fear, of a punishing or avenging deity, were essentially Christian doctrines, we should be compelled to answer this question in the affirmative.

It seems to us, however, that they are not essentially Christian doctrines, and further, that they seem inconsistent with what we conceive to be the essence of Christianity. (*Vide* John Macmurray, *Creative Society.*)

32.—TESTIMONY TO PSYCHOTHERAPY*
(By R. S. Allan)

The number of people anywhere who have been successfully treated by modern psychological methods is rapidly growing, but still not vast: and the number in New Zealand is as yet very small indeed.

Of these persons very few have been disposed to write or publish any account of the experience; and, of those so disposed, fewer still are qualified to give an adequate account of it in print. The writer of this pamphlet therefore is a member of a distinguished, but as yet very small, company. This is therefore a valuable essay, but it will perhaps require some discernment and imagination on the part of the reader to appreciate the value of this message.

—M. B. B.

THIS article is the result of very vivid personal experience which, I feel, involves at once a challenge and a responsibility. The responsibility is to share with others such understanding as I gained by my experience and the activities to which it led; and the challenge is to fight against those influences which might involve others in vicissitudes such as my own. Here, then, very briefly, are the reasons why a geologist, without training in academic psychology, presumes to write on principles of mental health.

* This section appeared in pamphlet form in 1946.

Some years ago I was persuaded to attempt to solve some personal difficulties' (which, incidentally, were thought to be of purely physical origin) by submitting myself to analytic treatment by a medical psychologist. It seemed to me at the time a counsel of despair. I knew nothing of psychological medicine, and I was being asked to plunge into unknown realms where reason, which as a scientist I prized, seemed to play a very minor rôle. The treatment was long—it lasted for rather more than three years—arduous, and costly. Progress was slow, particularly at first, and I fought bitterly to preserve the false façade I had built round my personality. Gradually, with painful slowness, unconscious conflicts emerged from the hidden recesses of my mind. Early emotional storms were relived with vivid intensity and the strength of pent-up forces dissipated. Hand in hand went a process of emotional re-education, until, at long last, I was enabled to reach some measure of emotional stability and mental health.

My experience, of course, is not unique, but it is as rare as it is unusual. For me it was at first devastating and humiliating, so much self-deception and so many false ideals had to be discarded, but it was also thrilling and invigorating in so far as one became a real person and the hideous handicap of soul-destroying anxiety and guilt faded into the background and disappeared. To it I owe what understanding I have of the underlying causes of mental ill-health and of the factors which make for mental health.

I learned, to my surprise, that mental ill-health, commonly termed ' nervous breakdown,' and technically neurosis or psychoneurosis (which is quite distinct from insanity or psychosis) is an illness in which the emotions—love, hate, anger, fear, guilt, etc.—play the major rôle. I re-experienced the unbelievable strength of the primitive emotions of love and hate during the re-living of early childhood conflicts. This was a salutary process, for most adults have completely forgotten such feelings and are inclined to minimize their significance, if not to question their existence. I witnessed at first hand the devastating effects on the adult personality of the repression of one or other or both facets of the early love-hate situation which follows deprivation or frustration of love. I saw, too, the way in which an intolerable load of guilt becomes attached to one of the conflicting impulses, and how this pattern persists into adult life. I felt the paralysing effect of anxiety and realized that it was this morbid fear which was the prime cause of mental ill-health. On the other hand I discovered—and this was pure gain—something of the healing qualities of love, and of the beneficent part played by a satisfactory and adequate love relationship in early childhood. I found that the need to feel loved was the basic requirement in child nurture.

The realization that mental ill-health was an emotional illness led me to a second discovery, namely, that my capacity to form close personal relationships was limited. I had sensed vaguely that my attitude to authority was not what it should have been, but I did not know why this was so. I found out that personal relationships involved the emotions, and that mutually satisfactory fellowship is possible only for the emotionally mature. I learned, too, that all later relationships were powerfully coloured for good or ill by the nature of the first love-relationship between mother and child. I found that if this first communion was marred in such a way as to produce feelings of deprivation and frustration in the babe, then that child would find it difficult to establish satisfactory relationships in adult life.

Perhaps the most unexpected thing I learned was that neurosis has its origin, its pre-disposing factors, in early childhood; that the precipitating factors which bring about the 'nervous breakdown' of later life represent but a part of the clinical picture; and that there might be a lengthy latent period between pre-disposing and precipitating causes. More important still, I discovered that medical psychologists had abundant evidence to show that the foundations of mental health were also laid in the first five years of life. This period of early childhood, then, becomes one of quite paramount importance. The emotional pattern of adult personality is determined, in the main, by experiences during the first five years of life.

Unexpected also was a slow realization of the potency of the unconscious as a motivating agent. Acts, decisions, points of view, which at first sight appeared to be based solely on reason, were, I found, powerfully influenced by wishes or motives which, in the beginning, were unconscious, and therefore beyond control. This was, at first, a humiliating discovery; one which appeared to threaten the primacy of the intellectual life as I knew it and valued it. I found that the reasoning' faculty was capable of staggering self-deception and that the mechanism of rationalization was commonly employed to disguise real motives.

Finally I learned something about the causes of neurosis, namely that the cardinal factor which prevents the development of mental health or emotional growth is faulty nurture. I felt, and feel, that in the two major discoveries of the medical psychologists—that is, the supreme importance of the early emotional life, and the crucial part played by nurture in the development of emotional maturity—lies the key to a great opportunity to remove or ease a burden which rests heavily on mankind.

While I was still receiving treatment I attended a course of lectures on ' Mental Health ' given, under the auspices of the Workers' Educational Association in Christchurch, by Dr. M. Bevan-Brown. The lecturer, a graduate of the Universities of Cambridge and New Zealand, had for some seventeen years, from 1923 to 1939, been one of the physicians at the Tavistock Clinic, London, and for most of that period had carried on private practice in psychotherapy in Harley Street. He had also been on the lecturing and supervising staff of the Tavistock Clinic, and had been closely associated there with Crichton-Miller and J. A. Hadfield. He had taken part in seminars with Jung, Adler, Stekel, William Brown and other eminent psychologists. He did not claim to belong to any of the chief schools of psychology, but seemed to be thoroughly acquainted with the doctrines and theories of all the schools and to have allowed due importance to each. The W.E.A. course was illuminating and stimulating. At the concluding lecture it was suggested that a club be established for the purpose of studying in greater detail the material of the lectures. This was the origin of the Mental Health Club,* which was affiliated to the Christchurch branch of the New Education Fellowship. Dr. Bevan-Brown was the first chairman, and has since been President of the Club which for a number of years has served as a centre for the discussion of problems relating to mental health and child nurture.

* Now ' Christchurch Psychological Society.'

For me this activity has been the means of gaining greater insight into many aspects of mental health. It has involved discussion of principles, reading of pertinent literature, consideration of case-histories, attempts at solving personality difficulties reported by members, and something of propaganda; it has meant discussing such topics as marriage, original sin, fear, love, aggression, homosexuality, masturbation and scores of others. It has been an invaluable opportunity to hear so able and well-qualified a man give so abundantly of his accumulated wisdom and experience in psychotherapy. Freely he has given to those who would hear, the quintessence of the subject. My feelings are those of Darwin when he wrote of his friend Charles Lyell, ' I always feel as if my books came half out of Lyell's brain and that I never acknowledge this sufficiently. . .'*

In addition to this, and under the direct guidance of Dr. Bevan-Brown, I have attempted to use the art of psychotherapy with cases of both civil and war neurosis. I claim, therefore, to write, not with authority, but with some understanding of the problems involved. and above all, with a burning sense of the importance of the subject.

The position as I see it is as follows. As a result of psychotherapeutic practice it has been possible to discover why, how and when neurotic persons became ill, and, at the same time, to see how these illnesses could have been prevented. In other words, it is now possible to indicate influences which make for neurosis, and, conversely to understand what is involved in adequate nurture which leads to mental health. The latter, of course, depends also on sound physical health and hereditary endowment, but for practical purposes early nurture is of greatest importance. Mental health is an affair of nurture—by which I mean the whole process of ' bringing up '; broadly the effect on the child of the impact of his physical and social environment; and, in particular, the influences of his parents and his home.

I am concerned pre-eminently with prophylaxis, that is with indicating the attitude of mind, or if you like, the way of life, which will lead to the prevention of neurosis and the less severe personality difficulties. Or to put it positively, my

* More Letters of Charles Darwin, Vol. II, 1903, p. 177.

aim is to indicate the conditions for the establishment of an environment in which each child can develop harmoniously to the full extent of his or her innate potentialities, i.e., in emotional maturity or mental health.

The reasons for this attitude are not far to seek. I am literally appalled not only by the incidence in our community of neurosis of disabling severity, but also by the high proportion of individuals who suffer in greater or lesser degree from emotional immaturity, whose personal relationships are twisted or faulty.

The crime of all this is that it need not happen. The neurotic is not responsible for his disabilities, he is the victim of his environment. The faulty nurture which warped his personality is part and parcel of our culture. This indictment of our culture is a serious one. If it is justified, the responsibility of those who realize the position is all the greater. They have the right, and the duty, to point to nurtural influences which, in susceptible cases, lead to full-fledged neurosis, or to less severe personality difficulties. This duty becomes clearer when it is recognized that treatment of neurotics will not solve the problem. The number that can be treated is but a small fraction of the total of the emotionally ill. What is needed, and most urgently needed, is an educational campaign designed to spread the principles of mental health throughout the community.

At the present time few realize the significance and potentiality for good in the discoveries of the medical psychologists, and many, for reasons which are not hard to find, are hostile to the implementation of the lessons to be learnt from them. This is easy to understand: first, because the principles of mental health derive from the investigations initiated by Freud and are comparatively new; secondly, because the implementation of the new teaching would conflict at once, and strongly, with deeply entrenched traditions and modes of thought. Dr. Bevan-Brown has pointed out that attempts to raise the standard of mental health 'would involve some profound changes in common conceptions in regard to the teaching of morality and discipline, and the general care of the young.'*

* Mental Health and Education, 1944, p. 1.

Yet here, I believe, lies the key to an era of happiness, health and security, such as the world has not previously known; here will be found the solution to many of the vexed problems of family life, in which emotional factors are so potently engaged, and which are responsible for so much misery and strife. Here, too, is the clue to the development of self-discipline and character upon which, in large measure, the survival of our civilization, or the growth of a better one, must depend.

I have this vision of things to come; a culture in which each person has a capacity for friendship, adequate courage, self-confidence, a capacity to love objectively, and a desire to contribute to the community of which he is a part; in short, a culture in which each person is mentally healthy, living a full life, unafraid, a good parent and a co-operative member of his social unit.

We want the right conditions for the growth of personality and character, which should be the main object of education. In this sense, education is synonymous with self-discipline, which is a method of control enabling one to be responsible for one's own conduct and for one's own decisions. But it is discipline by an active, healthy mind; it is control from within the individual. Such a discipline as this should result in a growth of judgment of social values; in an increase of confidence in one's self and in others; in greater self-respect; in feelings of security; in ability to co-operate; in harmony in personal relationships; in short, in emotional maturity.

We are far from this ideal, and the cure for this state of affairs is, as indicated, a matter of education. I believe that this education should aim first at the production of good parents and mentally healthy children. What is needed most is a ' new deal ' for very young children. This ' new deal ' is primarily a task for parents, and the necessary reforms must be reforms in child nurture in the home and in institutions and societies which offer guidance to parents. The key to reform is a clear understanding of the basic need of the child —the need to feel loved.

On the one hand, then, there is this vision of an ideal; on the other, the present deplorable state of affairs. If we look about us we find that our man-made environment and present conceptions of child nurture are responsible for untold misery and unhappiness. We live in a culture in which the majority of individuals are not living up to their full capacity; in which the family is too often broken or divided by feelings of anxiety, hate, jealousy and so on; in which parents dominate their children or vice versa; in which children are too often unloved, unwanted or neglected and ill-treated. We find everywhere nurtural conditions which prevent, or render difficult, the development of mental health. Worse than this, we see in operation over and over again the very factors which lead to personality disorders. Neurosis is being produced every day in our midst. The worst offenders are parents and members of those very institutions or professions whose job it is to advise parents concerning the bringing up of their children. Let me hasten to add that many, perhaps most, parents are doing their level best to give all they can to their children; and that the many organizations which set out to guide or instruct parents in this or that aspect of child welfare are animated by splendid motives, and staffed by individuals of the highest ideals and integrity. Yet, without doubt, neurosis is being produced in our midst every day by well-meaning parents, by teachers, by Plunket and Karitane nurses, by the clergy, and by doctors.

What then is the trouble? Where are we at fault? Fundamentally the trouble has arisen through our lamentable failure to understand the amazing intensity and importance of the young child's emotional life. All that the adult will be is potential in the emotional life of the very young child, and this development will take place harmoniously only under favourable conditions of nurture. If nurture is inadequate during early years, what is innate is dammed up, or inhibited, and the stage is set for neurosis or mental ill-health. The basic need of a young child is a satisfactory love-relationship with his or her mother. What does this mean? Love is a capacity for a mutual relationship with another person; a relationship involving the whole person, and in which emotional elements are potently engaged. It is found in early infancy in the breast-feeding situation, and is there the prototype of the later adult love-relationship. At its early stage it subserves nutrition; later it is linked with the reproductive instinct; in both situations it is highly sensuous,

83

Sensuousness is the dominant feeling in the early relationship, but maternal love also provides security and protection; the mother, in fact, supplies all the child's needs.

According to Dr. Partridge ' it is the clear understanding of this all-embracing fact that is the key to avoiding the mistakes which mothers have made in the past, and which have produced " difficult children " in untold numbers and brought havoc to many people's lives.'*

If something goes wrong, and it so often does, in this mutual love-relationship, for example, during breast-feeding, at weaning, or at other stages in child development, then troubles will commence, and grievous harm may result.

The child's basic need to feel loved gives us a criterion by which we may recognize faulty nurture. The young human baby is almost completely helpless, being utterly dependent on its mother. Any act or attitude, therefore, which fails to give the needed feelings of security, or which induces fear or inferiority feelings in the child, must be judged as harmful. A further point to be stressed is that if the mother shows in any way that she disapproves of the natural instinctive impulses which dominate the child's emotional life, trouble is certain. For example, if the mother herself is in a state of emotional conflict about breast-feeding; or if she is critical of, or disgusted by, the child's need for sensuous gratification, or by its aggressive impulses, then the child will feel unloved, insecure, and anxious. These feelings may become incorporated in the growing personality with damaging results.

These faulty attitudes and others such as scolding, blaming, punishing, hating, criticizing, etc., are extremely common and are responsible for emotional havoc in thousands of lives in our own community.

What, then, does the child require of its parents? First and foremost it needs to be loved for itself; it needs an atmosphere of security in which it can develop its instinctive impulses which are innate, spontaneous, natural, and healthy. The child needs to feel wanted; that he belongs and is part of a harmonious whole; to find in his parents a secure, dependable haven and a refuge from all danger. Negatively

* E. J. Partridge: *Baby's Point of View.* 1937, p. 30.

the parents must avoid making the child feel anxious, ashamed, guilty, unclean, inferior, or unwelcome.

We find many mothers, considerate worthy people whose greatest wish it is to give their best to their children, fail dismally to make these children feel loved, wanted and secure. Ignorance is rife, and ' difficult children ' are all too numerous. We find that many fathers fail even more dismally to play a rôle conducive to harmonious development. I have had experience of Plunket nurses and Karitane nurses whose knowledge of the child's emotional life was quite inadequate. I have had advice from a Plunket nurse which filled me with horror, and which if applied could only produce feelings of intense frustration, anxiety and insecurity in the child concerned. We have authenticated cases of forced feeding, of faulty weaning, of the infliction of punishment, of faulty handling at the toilet, and so forth, which fill us with dismay and despair.

I stress these faults because I have a great admiration for the Plunket Society and the work it is trying to do. If a sound training in the basic emotional needs of the young child could be added to the existing curriculum, and if the nurses were selected with greater regard for the emotional maturity of the individuals concerned, a great increase in the mental health of the community would certainly result. There is a duty here, and a responsibility, which those charged with the training of nurses cannot much longer neglect. There is also a splendid opportunity for adding most significantly to the mental health of future generations.

Some of the faulty attitudes mentioned are the result of attempts to enforce moral and religious teaching. Dr. Bevan-Brown has written, ' One of the most significant discoveries of modern psychological investigation is the danger of direct or explicit " moral training " and " moral teaching " to children, especially of pre-school age, but also in later childhood. Here " moral training " is understood to imply the express laying down of rules and principles of conduct; the definition of categories of " right " and " wrong " conduct and moral codes, i.e., the attempt to establish a system of morality by precept. These rules and principles are usually based upon some tradition or religious outlook and may also purport to be Christian.'*

In particular, certain types of religious teaching, especially those which tend to inculcate fear or guilt, may have disastrous effects on emotional development.

It was T. A. Ross who stated that basically the neurotics were people who had lost faith in themselves. It is certain that they suffer from an inability to form adequate personal relationships. This is a religious problem, if one believes that religion is ultimately concerned with personal relationships, with communion or fellowship. The clergy have a great rôle to play in this fight for a ' new deal ' for young children; and they can do a tremendous amount of good in innumerable homes, if they understand and accept the findings of medical psychologists. But if they accept this task, which is, after all, literally the cure of souls, they must first discard a modicum of traditional dogmatism.

I have said nothing yet about the teachers or the doctors. I have, however, indicated that education, self-discipline and mental health mean much the same thing, viz., the development of personality and character. I have also stressed the viewpoint that the fundamental elements of personality—those emotional and conative components which are concerned in mental health—have their foundation in the early years of childhood. Two important conclusions are inevitable. First, the function of the primary and post-primary schools is secondary in importance to that of the home and the parents. By the time a pupil enters the primary school his emotional pattern is largely determined for good or ill. All the school can do—and I do not under-estimate its importance—is to strengthen healthy tendencies and to modify in some measure those which are morbid. Here the crucial factor is the personality of the teacher. There is room for reform in this matter. I agree with Dr. Bevan-Brown when he writes that ' more attention should be paid to the personality of the teacher both in selection and in training so that it may be ascertained whether his (or her) influence on the emotional or personality development of the child is likely to be beneficial or harmful—this quite independently of his (or her)

* *Mental Health and Education.* 1944, pp. 6-7.

aptitude for teaching special school subjects in an efficient way.'*

The second conclusion I make is even more important. It is that if the community is really concerned with the growth of personality and character, i.e., with mental health, then far more attention should be paid to the nurtural factors which influence the pre-school child. Here the first five years of childhood are of crucial importance.

I will resist the temptation to write in detail of the doctors. There are those among them who have specialized in medical psychology and some of these are acknowledged leaders in child psychology; there are others who by accident of temperament are understanding and efficient psychotherapists even if they do not use an analytic technique; there are still others who although untrained have had to deal with war neurosis on a large scale and who, therefore, welcome and use the findings of psychology. But the great majority of ordinary general practitioners in New Zealand have had no formal training in psychotherapy, know nothing of it, and if not hostile because of their own conflicts, are at best lukewarm. This is a situation which cries aloud for reform. The danger —a very real one—lies in the fact that for centuries the doctor has inherited the mana and prestige of the ancient medicine-man. In these circumstances his advice is usually accepted and acted upon. But what if, in this field of the emotions, it is bad advice?

Doctors, clergy, nurses and social workers have wonderful opportunities for psychotherapy. They have this in common: that they have access, under privileged conditions, to many homes. They are often able to gain insight into the general home environment and not infrequently receive confidences which are hidden from the outside world. They are normally present during, or soon after, times of emotional stress. They are all made familiar with conditions of unhappiness, privation, financial worry, domestic strife, illness, and the thousand and one situations which call for sympathetic understanding and demand some kind of advice or action. They see how children behave towards their parents, and towards one another; and they see how parents deal with their children, and with one another.

* *Mental Health and Education,* 1944, p. 6.

In short, their opportunities for doing good—or harm—are tremendous. Each one of them would do a better job if he (or she) were familiar with the basic principles of mental health; if he (or she) would accept and act upon the fundamentally important truths: that the development of mental health depends on sound nurture; that the early years of childhood are crucial in this respect; and that the key to the whole problem is a recognition of the cardinal principle of mental health that the child must feel loved.

33.—REPORT OF A CASE OF ANXIETY STATE WITH PHOBIAS

(By a Member of the Christchurch Psychological Society.)

THIS case history in which the predisposing factor is a traumatic incident during breast-feeding is given in full with the consent of the patient concerned. The conditions under which the treatment was undertaken were unusual. The analyst was due to leave New Zealand for the United States ,almost immediately, and his objective was to relieve tension by palliative treatment.

The patient had been known to the analyst and his wife for many years; the latter had known him intimately from his birth. In the few months preceding the interviews here recorded, he had written in detail to her about his troubles and I had read the letters and made suggestions to her for her replies. In some measure, therefore, the stage was set. In addition to this there was rather a strong degree of hero-worship for the analyst.

The patient, still in his early twenties, had returned to New Zealand some months previously, after serving for some years in the Royal Air Force, where his main job had been ferrying bombers across the Atlantic. He had not been wounded, and during the war and at the time of treatment was physically in good health.

Throughout treatment he sat in an armchair in my study and no attempt was made at complete relaxation. He lived in my house as a member of the family.

In the verbatim account which follows, the patient's words are given as I wrote them down at the time. My questions 'and comments to him during the analysis were very few. Nothing significant is omitted. To eliminate the possibility of a reader identifying the patient I have altered place names and personal names. Capital X in the text stands for his fiancee.

ANXIETY CASE WITH PHOBIAS

P.—The whole thing is imponderable. I have imaginary ills. I am hypochrondriac—in particular, I fear venereal disease. The symptoms did not arise until I was coming home. I had my appendix out at sea. After that, fear got hold of me. There was some basis for it. I'd had an adventure with a girl in Glasgow. We got matey. I did not take her at all but afterwards I got a pimple on my tummy.

A.—Not on your penis?

P.—I was told by a doctor that everything was all right. The fears persisted. I had a blood test by a second doctor. It was negative. On the boat coming home the same thing happened with another girl. As the deed was about to be done I thought, ' I am a fool,' and cast it from me, but things were fairly intimate again. I saw a doctor again, and a blood test was negative. Well, that covered syphilis, but I feared gonorrhoea. There were no symptoms, no infection. I got upset again, saw another doctor. He assured me that there was nothing the matter, and therefore I dismissed my fears. Since that there has been no possibility of infection. Two weeks ago the fear came up again. I lost a lot of sleep—was worried and upset—went to another doctor. He said that I was mistaking normal functions for symptoms and assured me there was nothing to worry about so that settled it but the recurrence of the fear goes on.

I am dreaming a lot—sometimes the dreams are erotic. I carry on, in fantasy, with the things that might have happened. My hands are burnt, my face is bashed about. I see myself returning to the ship with a broken wing, trying to land disabled.

I had a dream last night in which X turned me down.

I had feelings of guilt and shame when I was returning home—an awful fear of what would happen by wrecking another life. I told X all about it. She said she trusted me

—she was not disgusted or disappointed. This pleased me. I am so scared of breaking that trust.

I worry about impotency. I don't know why. I have no evidence to believe that I will be impotent. I fear she will be unhappy. I was sexually precocious—I used to masturbate freely as a child and have not broken it yet. I tried to fight it for years. It's been very frequent since I came back. There were three months' spells while I was away when I did not masturbate but nothing like that since I have come home. I don't imagine myself with anyone—I am detached. It's all to do with me. It's a purely sensual few seconds.

A.—What do you feel about it?

P.—I've been a damn fool. I wish I didn't. I feel self-reproached—I have failed. I had a photo of X on the ship. On the photo I wrote ' No.' I felt ashamed for masturbating. I had broken a promise to her—she was a dream.

A.—Masturbation is only important as a symptom of a want of love.

P.—I am afraid I don't want X sexually. I am afraid I will seek solace in myself and therefore I will make her unhappy.

A.—Masturbation is a symptom of wanting something.

P.—There has always been something lacking—I can't find it. I don't know what it is—a feeling of being put aside—I don't know. I was always scared of the dark—I got terrible nightmares. Mother had to sleep with me. The light had to be turned on—murderous and fiendish things. I was being lowered into my grave—I was frightened of ghosts and murderers. I always wanted to get away from him. . . . At fourteen I wanted to join the navy—I was told not to be silly. I was a perfect fiend to my young brother. I gave him a hell of a time—smacked him on the head with a hammer. The strangest thing is that he and I have come together in a wonderful way. It no longer worries me that he was given preferential treatment.

I did not do well at school. Disappointment was expressed at that.

One Christmas I was in camp cooking. Mother jabbed me in the ribs. I jabbed her back. Dad was livid and I was told to get out. A piece of toast was thrown at me. I went into the bush for the day. I don't remember what I thought at the time. I was cast out. I wanted to get out. I always had a piggy temper. It's not entirely controlled now. I once bit a child's lip right through.

I was told very early that I must be above the average because my father was a professional man. The biggest hiding I ever had was given me wrongly. I was using the mower—I hit a stone—I put it away—I got a hiding for lying, and I didn't lie at all.

When I joined the army from a sense of duty I could see I was not going to get overseas until I was twenty-one. I was not sorry to go away. I lived! I was myself—not my father's son. I had a great time while I was away. I was trusted and given responsibility. I was a lieutenant at twenty-three—no mean accomplishment. I was rather cocky. Everything was great. I was proudly exhibited when I came home.

Then I was discharged. Wedding plans were put off and put off. First, it was to be Christmas—then to be February—then they said we'd have to wait four years: I must not spoil my academic career. That was the first consideration.

Mother said, 'X can't love you much if she won't wait.' Always they said 'You haven't the money.' In fact every objection was found.

A.—By father or mother or both?

P.—Father mostly—mother follows him. I said we could not wait. More objections. After that I issued my ultimatum. Plans were in progress, lots of discussion. All this coincided with the last fright I got. I want to get married more than anything else. Yet there are objections. I wonder if I will be able to support X, if I will be able to give her any children, if I will give her any dreadful disease. It all goes round and round and round.

A.—Is X bringing pressure to bear?

P.—She is very keen. She feels that we can't wait four years. She doesn't think she could last out that time. She's terribly disappointed each time it's postponed.

After I came home she was not entirely sure of herself. She was treated by the family as a daughter. Now she feels a usurper and she doesn't like going to my home.

I've really never made any decisions for myself in my life. My engagement was decided for me too. Dad went into X's

91

bedroom and said, 'It's time we did something about this. I will write to ——.' X was taken by surprise. I received a letter from Dad—a rare occurrence. It's always important. He told me everything was settled. X was willing. Everything possible would be done for me—not to worry about financial commitments. He would buy a ring which he has done, and refused to let me pay for it. When I got home the red carpet was rolled up very smartly—a complete change in attitude. I feel furious with myself. I tried to kid myself that it was unavoidable. I should have made a break. I want to be on my own to live my own life. I was very happy all the time I was away. I was very glad I didn't have to ask for a penny.

A.—What did you do about it?

P.—I didn't do anything. I just accepted it. The circumstances made me take it, but to be made a recipient of bounty—it irks me. I have always taken, taken, and it's always been given—a spider casting a web. It got X, too, good times, etc.—ring. . . . . Then she was scared I would grow up like my father.

A.—So 'furious with myself' is only partly true?

P.—I felt dependent. I hadn't the guts to strike out. I had lost my opportunity. I wasn't capable of breaking out.

A.—What is the feeling?

P.—I found it a bitter pill to swallow that after all these years I was still dependent. I was still a small boy. It's after the independence of the Fleet Air Arm. I feel second-rate, useless.

A.—Furious?

P.—It's a desire to break out—to make a clean sweep—to get away from it all—to have the things I want. My decisions were made for me again. It is slipped on like an old cloak. I'm just where I was before. I don't wish that. It was an intense dislike of what had gone on before. I tried to fight. It was self-reproach. It was a hate of the old order. I don't know that it is hate. It's unnatural. It's conventional to love, honour and all that. . . . My God! I hate him sometimes, domineering, brutal. He was an ogre. Now I hate to be in a room alone with him.

(Pause.)

Now that I can admit this to you I can remember other things. I remember you giving me a football—that was the greatest thing that ever happened to me. There is no pursuit in which we have anything in common. I don't get any pleasure with him—nothing in common—nothing at all.

Second Interview (next day)

Before I spoke the patient said:

What was the fear? I had been trying to find out what it was. It was a fear of light from the mirror. It was horrible to wake up and find my parents in bed with the light out. Even at school I saw pictures, kept me awake at night—lots of coffins—coffin lids—were-wolves—weird things, bats . . . someone was going to do something to me. I was going to be harmed. It is still there but I can tackle it. I cease to fear the terror. Sometimes it is an animal—an ape—a tiger—claws and talons—tears at my arm and shoulder.

A.—Think about this ape.

P.—I used to see it in the shadows—in the shape of clothes on the chair—in any freak of light in the early mornings—the moon shone in the window. I would attempt to hide under the bedclothes and then look out. It would still be there. I would assure myself that it was nothing. I would get out of bed and feel the clothes. When I had a light over my bed it was the nicest thing that ever happened to me. My God! It's not so long ago. It's huge and smelly.

A.—What sort of smell?

P.—Stale sweat. Oh. like a dirty dog. Can't bear the smell of unwashed dog. It comes over and stands by the bed. I try to get away. It envelops me. I attempt to fight it—get all mixed up in the blankets. I am often wakened with the bed disarranged, fighting, struggling with something, but no dream. Just this something that smothers me and wraps itself round me. It's round my neck and shoulders, grips my arms. I try and fight free.

At school I once had a crystal set and earphones. I went to sleep. I woke with the cord round my neck and nearly died with fright.

I always look round the house if I am alone. I am not happy by myself—sneaking shadows, creaks coming close.

A.—What has happened to the ape?

93

P.—He developed into a man when I realized that there were no apes in New Zealand. He took the form of a man with a knife. He lacerated me—drew it across me like an ape with claws—across my chest. I lie and hold my breath, pretend that I am dead—breathe into the pillows so he would not hear it.

A.—Describe the man.

P.—No, I can't. He is indeterminate. He was always in the house—never outside.

A.—Describe this knife.

P.—It was not large.

A.—Shape?

P.—Like a pocket-knife—did not extend beyond his hand—sort of hidden. It was the smashing—the leaping on to the bed—the attempt to fight. I would be mutilated. It was not the fear of death.

It was the same during the war. I knew I was coming back, but I feared mutilation.

A.—What part of you?

P.—My chest and throat—shoulders—perhaps the thigh. In the air I feared a broken shoulder or thigh—that I would damage it—so that I would not be able to manage the aircraft. It was always the left side.

A.—What is the significance of that?

P.—The left hand was the throttle hand. I am weaker on the left side—a freak of birth or something. I had an X-ray on discharge—curvature of the spine—undeveloped on the left side. It was pointed out to me when I was young—which has always worried me. I am always thinking of my carriage. It brought ridicule to me at school—so did my size.

A.—Why the thigh?

P.—Oh, it's important in the air. The thigh did not come in before because the rest of me was under the bedclothes.

My life at school was minor hell because of my carriage. There was a bloke at school I hated—fat greasy swine! He thrashed me awfully once. I have hated him always with real hatred.

A.—Come back to the ape, please.

P.—The eyes are the most distinguishing thing, and the animal smell. The eyes just look in at me—then he would pounce on me. He was shrouded. He leaped. I remember when a cat came in and out of my bedroom. It jumped on to my bed. I nearly passed out. Mum had to come in and sleep with me. Very agile animal. . . .

Main thing was the looking at me—the rising up and coming down. I would lie there petrified—not daring to shut my eyes.

A.—What do you think it means?

P.—I don't know. I can't place anything symbolic on it. I assumed it was normal. I wondered if I were a bit queer. I was always teased as a curiosity. The facts of my birth were told to me at an early age. I had nearly wrecked the issue. There was a malformation of my head. I had a scar on my forehead and the back of my neck where a bone was squashed. When it came to a decision—Mother or me—it was to be Mother. This was Dad's decision. I felt that I was more trouble than I was worth. I have often felt that I was conceived before they were married.

A.—That is not so in fact.

P.—It was only my bedroom that gave me the frights. Contemplation of suicide comes into the picture hundreds of times. I picture myself crashing a car—jumping over a bridge. I take my fiancée too, deliberately run the car over a bank.

A.—What do you think this means?

P.—It means ' give up the battle.' Things are too intolerable to bear any longer. It's the final form of self-punishment. I'm not worthy. I have thrashed myself. I've been terrible to X at times. She knows there is a conflict. She wants to help me take it away.

Dad makes Mother very unhappy often—small things—arguments. I always took Mother's side. Hypocrisy—we have to be so right. I am in perpetual vigilance. He has no finer feelings—no love of music—or things I might be interested in. We were to be seen and not heard.

(At this point I remembered a story received from my wife about an occasion when his father in company had taken a pair of deer's antlers from the wall—threatened the child and got an intense reaction of fear. I asked him to associate on these antlers.)

P —I don't remember antlers. I remember an affair of pig's tusks. No. I can't think. I've never been free with animals. I'm scared of horses—dogs put the fear of death into me. He used to go shooting every year.

A.—Associate on the pig's tusks.

P.—They are the large canines of the ape. They're capable of tearing and ripping like a bullet wound that tears through the flesh.

Third Interview (next day)

The patient reported that in the mid-afternoon during a walk with my small son he had had a sudden uprush of fear about the pig's tusks. He realized he was sweating. I asked him to try and recapture the feeling. He said:

I deliberately put myself back to try to find out the cause of the fear. I felt the need to wrap myself up—to draw my coat collar close. The feelings were about my shoulders. I felt cold under the arms. I realized I had sweated. There was an acrid smell ten minutes later. I was trying to place a connection. There was an abhorrence of the idea of the tusks. Then it all stopped.

The focus of the attack I feared was about the neck and shoulders and chest and the back between the shoulder-blades. A car came by and I realized I was not in the depths of the jungle but in the streets of Christchurch. I wanted . . . I don't know what it was going to do.

(Pause.)

Fear of mutilation—tearing.

A.—What did you think of between these statements?

P.—It is so close. I am trying to dig deeper. The fear is there. I have just come to a brick wall.

A.—Just focus on the tusks.

P.—They're ripping and tugging and grinning. There's a leer on the face—a pouncing—a fight—a struggle. I am torn in the process.

A.—Are you fighting?

P.—Yes, struggling, but it is too big. It smells foul. It's pressing my head against it. It's smothering me. Anything is protection—if I don't breathe—am quiet—if I appease it—but it refuses to be appeased. It rises and glares.

(*Patient fingering his lips*): It's like a bear, rising and grasping and smothering and then tearing—walks on its four legs and then rises up. It glares and bounces. I am looking at it from my bed—helpless—utterly petrified. It goes up and up.

A.—What are your lips doing?

P.—Closed and still. I can't see—desperately trying not to move or betray my presence. I lie perfectly still. If I hear a movement I know it's a great relief.

If I come home from anywhere at night and go round the back to the toolshed I race in, whistling like fury.

A.—Come back to the struggle and the foul smell.

P.—It's a smell of animal—furry coat of some sort, strong stale mustiness—unclean and dirty beast. That was what I was so smothered in. It had come on top of me.

A.—The smell of faeces?

P.—Yes (*but very uncertainly*)—more of a sweaty smell —not faeces, hot, doggy smell—acrid and bitter.

A.—Return to ' It's pressing my head against it.'

P.—Arms around me and pressed against its breast—it's there the smell comes in.

A.—What sort of breast?

P.—I am smothered in it and I can't breathe. I cry for help—I am pressed harder than ever—I waggle my head and try to get away. The harder I struggle the tighter I get. I'm being hurt by the pressure.

A.—Where?

P.—Across the shoulder—I'm fighting to lift my head away. I can't lift my head sideways. I'm trying to get away from it.

A.—It?

P.—It's getting more natural. It's not an ape at all. It's mother. Yes, it is. I've got my head between her breasts and I can't get clear. Breast on each side of my face—my God!

(Patient breaks down and weeps copiously. After an interval he says): I'm sweating like a pig.

(He then pulled himself together and went on):

It's a soft mass. It's the breast all right and I've got my head in between. I see it easily. I'm fighting, pummelling— I'm banging with my fists trying to get my head clear so that I can breathe. I'm smothered by this breast and clothes.

A.—Where does the smell come in?

P.—It's the erotic smell—acrid, sweaty, sharp, tangy

body-sweat. It's overpowering. I fight away from it. I can't get my head clear. There's this massive breast and I'm fighting away from it. Clothes are all messed up in it. I want to hurt it. I fight back—I pummel with my fists, heaving away with my hands. Pressure is against me—my fists are tight—pounding.

A.—Lips now?

P.—I'm yelling, crying—I'm fighting for it, for the comfort. I am in a wrong place—there's something I want. I fight away for it. I struggle for something—yes, to reach and climb up. I can look up and see—I'm being disregarded. The face is turned away—all I can see is the underside of the chin. I am lying with my head on the left and my head is here in the middle—too low—too low. I am beating it. One breast is too low and I am pummelling at it. The other is too high and I am being disregarded. There's talk going on. I am trying to attract attention and there's a smell. Clothes are getting in the way. Everything is in a hell of a state. I'm being held too tight and I can't reach. I want to hurt it to call attention. Face is still turned away. All I can see is the underside of the chin and nose turned to the left.

It's just a struggle and being in the wrong place. I'm between and across and the head is wrong. I feel softness and try to get away from the smell between the breasts. I want the nipple—I'm prevented. I'm disregarded. The face is turned away. I'm trying to get it to look down. It won't. I am left to struggle on my own. I have been deprived of my livelihood. I am hungry—I'm thirsty—my face is all screwed up. Oh, I can't get my head clear.

(Pause.)

I don't think there is any more.

Fourth and Final Interview (next day)

Patient reported feelings of relief and calm. It was like taking a great breath and letting it go.

P.—I got a fright yesterday. To-day I am quite sure I will never get a fright like that again.

Someone made a mistake originally which upset me greatly

emotionally. I can see the connection all the way through as clearly as possible.

(I then took the main symptoms—phobias, suicide, fear, impotency, inferiority feelings, masturbation, temper—and linked them up with the material which had appeared in the analysis.)

Psychopathology

When, why, and how·did he become ill, and why was he cured? The analysis was so short—the material so prolific and condensed that a clear picture of the psychopathology is difficult. The predisposing event was the smothering at the breast. Are we to assume that his whole life was ruined by one incident of possibly a few minutes' duration? The answer is obviously '' No.' In view of the difficult birth he was probably an anxious child from birth. Even if we discount the possible significance of a birth trauma, it is more likely that the whole breast-feeding situation was unsatisfactory, although the evidence at this point is not clear. What is most evident is the fear that he will be suffocated, with only a flicker of his sensuous desire, which is deeply repressed. That desire was permanent and it is that desire which keeps anxiety alive. Frustrated desire is present all the time. The venereal disease phobia contains the idea of punishment and guilt. In any sensuous situation there is panic, insecurity, and anxiety. ' I must be bad—this sensuousness and aggression must be bad.' Why should the fear be sustained and persist in various phobias? If the fear occurs with strong instinctive desires at a point in time it becomes permanently associated with it. For example: ' If I feel like this and act like this these terrible things will happen.' So therefore there is conflict.

The smell is the dominating impression—the ape symbol represents what is bestial, low, and smells. Smell was the centre of desire unconsciously, but consciously, the reverse—again conflict. The infant in a normal condition is sucking or sleeping. It is all mouth. If there is frustration the first reaction is rage—tearing and biting—tooth and fang. So fangs symbolize frustration plus rage.

If it appears that the mother is hostile or indifferent, she being automatically perfect, ' she doesn't want to feed me, therefore these feelings I have are nasty, and I must never have them.' The whole situation was equivalent to complete desertion by the mother, and smothering was the crucial episode. How was he cured?

The stage was largely set by previous association with the analyst. There was .hero-worship. Mother- and father-substitutes were available. All this plus extraordinary courage.

Later History

Patient returned to his home. told his father the whole story, suggesting that a better relationship was possible in the future. He married happily, is now a father. and has made steady progress with his academic work. and there has been no recurrence of symptoms.

Note on the Preceding Case (by M. B.-B.)

This case is· quoted in full because of its special interest. It is primarily included as illustrating the source of adult neurosis in first year experiences. But it has also another notable interest. The total time of treatment was four sessions. In this time what appears to be an experience at the breast was recovered which apparently was crucial as a predisposing cause of neurosis.

Normally. analytical treatment which 'gets back' to first year experiences occupies not less than three months. and frequently occupies three years.

Perhaps the purists will contend that this was not an analysis. We will not debate this with them. But. analysis or not. in this incredibly short space of time such an early experience was recovered.

When this case was first reported to me I also was incredulous, and doubted whether such things could happen. I was like the man who. seeing a giraffe at the zoo. said 'There's no such animal!' Or like myself. when I first saw the Empire State Building in fact. said. 'It couldn't be built. . . .'

But eighteen months have now elapsed since the end of treatment, and the patient has never looked back. He is now. I believe, happily married. so I must accept the facts presented to me.

From the point of view of analytical treatment it is to be noticed that many circumstances were extremely favourable.

e.g. (1) The patient's strong confidence in the analyst as a person and as a psychotherapist, and (2) that the patient himself, in the process of treatment, showed an unusually high degree of courage. Apart from this the result reveals a very high degree of analytical skill, insight, and intuition on the part of the analyst. This is only partly evident in the text because all tone of voice, expression, and gesture are necessarily absent.

For the same reason, the expressions of the patient will seem to the uninitiated much less impressive and dramatic than they really were: as spoken, they were charged with emotion, frequently intense emotion, which of course, cannot be reproduced in print.

As regards, the psychopathology—the dénouement suggests that the 'smothering' incident was the essential and sole predisposing cause of the neurosis. Neither the analyst nor I believe this. If it were so, it would mean that any person's life might hang upon such a thread as a fortuitous experience of temporary smothering. It is more than probable that the child was anxious and insecure from birth: his mother had nearly died in labour, and may be presumed to have been too ill and exhausted to provide him with adequate security and sensuousness in the early weeks. The ambivalent attitude to 'smell' indicates an intense conflict between sensuous desire and fear.

The smothering incident brings the conflict to a focus.

34.—THE FIRST SIX MONTHS—PSYCHOLOGY OF THE INFANT

(By Enid F. Cook)

An infant cannot reason, or think in the adult sense, but undoubtedly he can feel, and does feel intensely. After nine months' intra-uterine life where he has been warm, secure and quiet, he is projected into a vast bright space with countless alarming experiences overtaking him. The first feeling, then, that he is prone to have is fear. Some would prefer the term 'anxiety' here. This fear or anxiety will vary in intensity according to his own inherent sensitivity and to the manner in which he is treated and handled. At the same time he has an intense need for re-association with that being from whom he has been abruptly separated. This need is for the most intimate association possible with a person who has, or should have, a unique feeling towards him—his mother. If his need is met adequately, and as soon after birth as possible, his fear will be allayed. Observe the contrast of behaviour and manifestation of feeling in a new-born infant when being handled and bathed—tense and terrified, then snuggling down in his mother's arms and finding her breast, where a sense of well-being, comfort and satisfaction transforms his whole person and leads soon to relaxation. Here is certainty and safety, and here he learns to smile with confidence because someone loves him and comprehends completely. All this, provided that his mother is really adequate to her function. If she is really adequate and not narcotized, the infant may experience little, if any, fear. If she is inadequate and his need is not met, he will fall into fear, and this is dangerous for him. Also, if thus frustrated, he may feel rage as well as fear. This rage may become so intense that it becomes terrifying and reinforces the fear previously resulting from deprivation. Such a state if not speedily corrected may seriously interfere with breast-feeding. Normally his waking hours should be occupied in a satisfactory intimate relationship with his mother, into which fear does not enter—and rage very little. In the intervals he normally sleeps.

In the first nine months sensuousness and dependence are his dominant traits, and his main occupation is feeding and sleeping. The avoidance of anxiety in these early months is essential to the mental health and future development of the child. The avoidance of anxiety involves the attainment of security and confidence through intimate association with an adequate and competent mother who is herself free from anxiety. As part of this association breast-feeding is essential, as well as the need for the mother to be within earshot of the baby during his sleeping hours throughout the first years. He should never be allowed to cry without attention. It is not necessarily desirable to pick him up each time he cries; a voice of reassurance or a touch will often suffice.

Breast-feeding has the priority because it supplies the best environment for the child. He must not at this stage be fitted into an adult household regime, as is suggested by following a strict four-hourly timetable. He has an individual rhythm which can be gauged by a mother who is attuned to her child, and who is not made over-anxious by the advice of outsiders. A baby who feels secure will not cry to be fed unnecessarily, but an anxious child will feel the need of such comfort. It is not nourishment so much as reassurance that he is seeking.

In the earliest days of his life he is not aware of his mother as a person, but is certainly aware of the warm, soft breast as something essential to his well-being. It is his property, and from it he can derive adequate satisfaction of all his instinctive urges. But the presence behind the breast is all-important. Pleasure cannot be experienced in this intimate procedure unless mother is in tune. It needs to be a mutual physical pleasure satisfying to both, two persons enjoying each other. This is love in embryo.

What if mother finds breast-feeding a difficulty? What if she considers it an unpleasant duty, something rather crude and akin to animal behaviour which she despises? If her own sensuous feelings are involved in conflict and she finds no pleasure in the experience, the child becomes aware of something lacking.

His whole existence depends on sucking, which is most comforting to him, and if this is not approved of by the mother, he may suck more frantically or he may refuse the breast. Anxiety is infectious and can be caught from the mother. If unrelieved, it will persist as an attitude to life. A train of symptoms is set up such as ' windy spasms,' irregular bowel movements, poor appetite, thumb sucking, restless sleep, and so on.

The extreme dependence of the infant is sufficient reason for the principle of keeping the child close to the mother. This is eloquently endorsed by Dr. Joyce Partridge in her book *Baby's Point of View*, written out of a wealth of psycho-analytic experience. Her fourth axiom in the practical handling of infants is, ' Never leave a baby alone to cry.'

Mother is the original object of all infantile feelings, and the younger and more helpless the child, the more intense and concentrated are his feelings. No one else feels or sounds the same as mother. When this is properly appreciated, responsible people will avoid creating situations where mother is not available, and thereby avoid much anxiety and subsequent ill-health. The most helpless moment in the whole of life is surely at birth. In those first hours of life nothing can compensate for that first separation as satisfactorily as the mother's arms and the mother's breast. It is not always necessary to nurse the child, for the presence of mother is often enough.

In *The Nursing Couple* Dr. Merell Middlemore records her observations of the behaviour of a series of breast-fed infants. She notes how essential enjoyment is to the satisfied suckling, and how this is related to the careful handling by the mother. She suggests that as the nurse has not the maternal relationship to the infant, she may be an unwelcome intrusion between mother and child. A minimum of handling is also important.

35.—HOW DOES BREAST-FEEDING FEEL FROM THE MOTHER'S POINT OF VIEW?

(By Enid F. Cook)

DR. Bevan-Brown has stated that in the breast-feeding relationship the baby *knows* whether the mother is enjoying the ' process and him,' or not. He asks me as a mother to confirm this, and whether I have any suggestions as to *how* the baby knows. I can confirm the statement, but can only surmise that there is an intimate response from the nipple to the mouth. Prof. J. C. Spence, of Newcastle-on-Tyne, emphasizes the fact that a mother should be able to fall physically in love with her baby as soon as possible after the birth of the child. He says they should be in as close contact as possible, skin to skin. In this way, the baby is aware of the sheltering comfort of the mother. If she falls physically in love with her baby she desires above all to hold it closely. The baby feels the warmth and comfort of her body, and as he snuggles up and finds the nipple he can sense by the way she gives herself to him that she is enjoying being drawn upon. She makes it comfortable and easy for him to get what he wants, she watches and listens and holds him close. He can tell by her attention and interest and by all the tokens of maternal love. He can feel her approval of his grunts and gestures, he hears her voice making pleasant sounds, he later sees her smile and nod. He comes to know by all the means of human communication that mother enjoys his demands upon her.

Because of his utter helplessness it is necessary for her to make the first approach, so he cannot love her until she loves him, and because she loves him she will want to give herself to him. The intense sensuous enjoyment in the breasts as the baby draws the milk can only be produced by the child. Thus a breast-pump used for the same purpose has not the same feeling, because it is a purely mechanical device instead of a personal relationship.

This sensuous experience is interpreted differently by different women. To those whose sensuousness is repressed it may be interpreted as painful. To the healthy maturing woman it is an added delight which is reflected in her whole feeling-tone. There is a heightening of awareness in her abdomen where the baby has so lately lain, and over the ovarian and uterine areas. Her skin, which is rightly regarded as an organ of emotion, receives a whole series of new stimuli through the baby's approach to the nipple, while the nipple, as the centre of this new experience becomes comparable with the vagina as a recipient of erotic stimulation.

By the avoidance of suckling her child, the woman is unwittingly depriving herself of a whole range of sensuous enjoyment, with subsequent relaxation and satisfaction. The barrage of negative advice which takes no account of the sensuous needs of women, regarding merely the time-saving and other such secondary factors, has thus led to an impoverishment incalculable in its ultimate effects.

So to return to our question. 'How does the baby know whether the mother is enjoying the breast-feeding process or not?' If he is the agent by which highly pleasurable sensations are excited in the mother's nipple, that organ will be stimulated and erect, and the automatic sucking action gives mutual pleasure until both are satisfied. If, on the other hand, the mother's sensuousness is repressed, and she shrinks from giving herself to the child, the novel sensation of being drawn upon is interpreted as painful. The nipple, instead of responding, is dry and flaccid, and the whole process is spoilt for the baby because the sensation in his mouth is unsatisfactory. The tumescence which accompanies the act of copulation must be present in the nipple, so that it is alive and sensitive, then all feels well and the baby's first sensuous and first love relationship develops healthily.

Any good mother if asked 'Does your baby enjoy breast-feeding?' will say 'Of course he does,' without being able to specify how she knows. On reflection one recalls the impatient anticipation before feeding when the baby seeks with his mouth for the object of his desire, nuzzling his head against the mother's body, burrowing blindly in an effort to bury his face in the soft familiar mass, but not satisfied until his mouth has reached the sought-for goal. Then how he fastens on, and starts the instinctive sucking that gives such a feeling of contentment as with eyes closed and jaw and tongue and lips hard at work, he feels the warm, sweet stream flow delectably downwards. When he gets into his stride, the striving gives place to a rhythmical grunt with every mouthful, the body relaxes and the little hands start to wander round, fondling or just touching the breast, to enhance his pleasure. After the first five or ten minutes his hunger and feeling of need is appeased and the sucking becomes less intense—he may even sink slowly into a contented drowsy state. His need was not merely for the prescribed ounces of milk but for that union and satisfaction of belonging; this need having been met, there is nothing more required, and he can return to temporary oblivion to continue his growth.

Alison was a premature infant taken to a babies' hospital and given her first feeds while lying in her cot. When returned to her mother and the breast she was emotionally most disturbed. The mother came anxiously to the doctor because of the child's 'paddy.' She was touchy and easily started crying with rage, which kept the whole household in a turmoil. She had been given orange juice and adexolin and various fluids out of a bottle in hospital, and was protesting violently against all these intrusions. The doctor suggested 'nothing but the breast—in private, and whenever she wants it.' At five months she is a happy thriving infant still fully breast-fed and good-tempered, but still positively declining to have anything out of a bottle. It just doesn't feel right. A remark of Prof. J. C. Spence is pertinent here: 'If nature had intended new-born infants to have water before the milk comes, a third nipple would have been provided, secreting a weak solution of lactose and water.'

In a Study of Breast-Feeding in a Mining Town, by Dr. Enid Hughes, reported in the *British Medical Journal* of September 25, 1948, it is stated by an experienced midwife that 'early weaning is much more likely where the mother is living with her in-laws. In such cases there is little chance of privacy, *the mother is embarrassed* at exposing her breast before her mother-in-law and possibly other members of the family. *The sense of outraged modesty* affects the baby who begins to whimper, and in a few minutes the mother-in-law will say, "That's not feeding the bairn, you'll want to get summat that'll satisfy it. Gi'e't summat in a bottle."' The sense of outraged modesty' (that is, feelings of fear and guilt) affects the baby—he is not satisfied because it doesn't feel right if mother is not enjoying the process and he is not given the indispensable ingredient that makes breast-feeding worthwhile. So he begins his bottle life, which subsequently fills the pockets of brewers and the manufacturers of soft drinks; the second best, which fails to meet so many of his basic needs. Another midwife of twenty-two years' experience in this Northumberland district says that a large number of mothers 'know breast-feeding is the right thing, but they won't be tied.'

When the baby has been kept waiting or mother is abstracted, he will suck violently as if wanting to get the whole breast into his mouth, and may almost choke with the effort. He is trying to get something from mother—not milk, but a response. Again, analyses of adults who are unequal to life's demands show the terrific intensity of this feeling of frustration and rage against the mother who is inadequate. The young mothers who 'can't be bothered' little realize the damage they are inflicting on the little life whom no one else can succour in the way that they can if they will.

During a deep mental analysis of a middle-aged spinster whose complaint was lifelong masturbation and inability to make friends, she came repeatedly to a picture—'I could just about paint it. Mother sitting on the side of a bed, I'm just in a cot and longing to be at her breast, but she is talking to father, and cross and tired, and she just gives me a bottle—that's the beginning of going without Mother— getting comfort of the second-best—that's what makes me crabby—that's where the hurt feeling comes from—the second-best—just like masturbation.'

This experience can be multiplied indefinitely, and if such

suffering can be prevented by more adequate motherhood, it behoves us to bend all our energies into the production of better mothers for more children in every generation.

I now append illustrations of this same contented mutual comfort reported by more recent mothers. The first is from an ex-teacher, mother of three children:

I (By J. P.)

'Before my first baby Susan was born I had been told and had read in *Baby's Point of View* and similar books that breast-feeding was enjoyable. I started feeding her with the idea that I would enjoy the experience, but I thought I was going to enjoy it *mentally*—not *physically*, with the result that the breast-feeding was not successful; nor was it much better with my second child. By " not successful " I mean that neither mother nor child enjoyed it. Susan chewed and wouldn't suck, and I would force her to have it because I *knew* it was a good thing, not because it was a pleasure. The second child Clement enjoyed his feeding. Always at the end of his feed his penis was erect and I could only assume that this was the result of the pleasure he had experienced. I was pleased with his pleasure but was not really sharing in it.

'Both were breast-fed for seven to eight months with some complementary feeding. I felt that this complementary feeding was bewildering, but a psychiatrist assured me that the child would have been even more bewildered with no breast-feeding at all.

'Before the third child arrived I had seen the results of my mistakes and was by then firmly convinced that the ideas I had been taught were really true, but my rage often prevented me from carrying them out. Some emotional readjustment was effected by a short course of treatment, and my third baby is a tremendous success! While I was still in the nursing-home there was the beginning of real physical enjoyment for me during breast-feeding. This was comparable to feelings experienced during coitus and in the same genital area.

'Having felt this myself, I have told three other mothers what to expect and just how the pleasure really feels. These women are now each happily breast-feeding their own children and the first thing they said to me when they saw me after their confinements was how true they discovered my words to be. Had it not been pointed out to them, they would probably have missed the significance of the possible mutual enjoyment. In each instance they have been made aware of the pleasure they would experience, and I remembered in my own case that with the second baby I could have experienced this if only I had recognized it and responded to the child's physical approaches. I repeat, my third baby is a tremendous success and I feel sure it is greatly due to the pleasurable breast-feeding and my own emotional development.'

II (By H. B.)   4th June, 1949.

' It was an unfortunate happening in a nursing-home. which greatly affected the psychological adjustment of our second child, that made my husband and me decide to have this. our third child, at home where we could put into practice all the things we felt were most important in the early nurture of a new baby.

' He was the product of a natural labour without anæsthetic or drugs of any kind in the Grantly Dick Read method of childbirth. I felt physically well and strong when our baby was born. While still attached to the cord he was handed to me, seven pounds of struggling tension, yelling lustily. His cries seemed to me to be obviously those of real fear. I felt deeply moved as I loved him, skin to my skin. Soon his crying and snuffling and burrowing ceased and he lay against me relaxed and still.

' The nurse then fixed the cord and he was put into his warm cot. While he lay making tiny noises I expelled the placenta without effort. In another five minutes he was given to me again to see if he wished to feed. He was held again with his skin against mine, his back wrapped in a muslin napkin. He at once opened his mouth and after a few seconds experimenting. took a firm hold of the nipple and sucked firmly and strongly for about ten minutes. Whilst feeding him I felt utterly content and happy and full of most tender love for the tiny new life which had so lately come into the world. After feeding he slept soundly in his cot for from four to five hours. after which time he was awakened to be bathed.

' Among the things that we felt important from the baby's viewpoint was the fact that his *hands should be free* so that he could fondle the breast if he wished, and that if he wished he could derive comfort from the sucking of his own skin. In the first week, at times when he was hungry and occasionally when he was first put back into his cot after feeding, he would get obvious pleasure and comfort from sucking his hands.

' The point we felt perhaps most important was the fact that the baby should *never be left alone to cry.* Our baby lay in his cot at my bedside. From time to time and for no apparent reason he would cry out suddenly with great urgency, obviously a cry of fear. I would lift him at once, and if a pat would not comfort him, I would cuddle him against my face and shoulder. If the cry was one of fear as I have already mentioned, a cuddle would rarely pacify him, so I would lay him with his hands and face on my bare chest. There, he would snuffle and rub his face on my skin while I would love and comfort and talk softly to him. Very soon his crying would stop, he would take a big jerky breath (as a child does after prolonged crying) and his tense little body would relax as he released a long, relieved sigh. He would then lie still on my chest and fall deeply asleep. Seldom did I find this procedure fail. On the few occasions when it did, he was put to the breast, where he would suck urgently. Then in a minute or less would come the jerky, indrawn breath followed by a great sigh and complete release of tension.

' I noticed that these sudden fearful cries were often followed by the child urinating. This usually occurred while I held and comforted him. It is interesting to note that as it had been my habit to talk softly to him as I loved him, after the first two weeks the sing-song sound of my voice alone will often stop a minor crying spasm.

' The third point we felt of great importance was that he should be allowed to feed when he wished and *establish his own breast-feeding routine.* Here we found that he slept a great deal for the first two days and wished to be fed about six-hourly. This interval gradually decreased in the next few days till he put himself on to a three-hourly schedule (with longer intervals at night) gradually passing to a four-hour routine with a five- or six-hour spell at night. By the end of the third week on his four-hourly routine he was sleeping with a break of eight and sometimes ten hours at night. His hunger cry was easily recognizable and rarely did I have to feed him outside the rough outline schedule mentioned above.

' Feeding time is a most happy and satisfying time for both of us—a period of relaxation and contentment. On coming to the breast he shows none of the anxiety and urgency which was so apparent in our second child. He calmly grips the nipple and sucks firmly and rhythmically, with great intentness of purpose, till he has finished. Then he lets the nipple slip from his mouth. Feeding takes on an average from twenty minutes to half an hour. I have never hurried his feeding by the partial withdrawal of the nipple. He has always fed at his own speed, stopping and starting as he wished.

' He has never vomited, and winds come easily, usually without need for patting; the latter point so happily different from the painful windy spasms of my other children. After feeding he often looks slightly dazed with utter contentment and he is often asleep as his head touches the pillow. At ten weeks of age he weighed 13 lbs. 4 ozs., two pounds above the average weight of that age on the N.Z. Plunket graph. This baby rarely cries and when he does the reason is always easy to find; so different from the seemingly unaccountable crying spells of my other two children at this age.

' This child in fact is a really ' good ' baby, secure in his environment and most contented and happy. Beneath his responsiveness and activity seems to be a basic calmness in which he shows no sign of strain and anxiety. He happily sustains, with equal equanimity, the clumsy loving of his young brother and sister, loud noises, cot bumping, and even in the past, an unpleasant nasal catarrh.

' We do not find it difficult to explain to our own satisfaction the reason why this baby differs so markedly from our other two children as babies. The main factors contributing to this happy state of affairs seem to us to be:

' *First.*—Natural, undoped childbirth. Consciousness at birth resulting physically in my feeling extremely well and strong; emotionally in my being a better mother and feeling an infinitely greater tenderness and love for the child who was truly mine from the start.

'*Secondly.*—By never allowing the child to be really frightened when it cried, resulting in the apparent complete lack of anxiety symptoms.

'*Thirdly.*—The self-regulated feeding methods resulting in the fulfilment of the basic needs of the child.

'*Fourthly.*—The complete absence of bowel training. (This point previously taken for granted.)

'I have never overstimulated this child as I was inclined to do with my other babies. Also, being born at home, he has been one of the family from the start and is much loved by both his young brother and sister. Those teaching the usually accepted child-rearing methods of to-day would expect this child, with his lack of habit-training to be a "spoilt, cross, exacting little tyrant." Happily this is not the case. We have a child who is and feels truly loved.'

June. 1949.

36.—AFTER-PAINS AND EARLY BREAST-FEEDING
(By Enid F. Cook)

THERE is accumulating evidence to show from enquiry of mothers that the 'after-pains' dreaded by so many women delivered in hospital are almost entirely obviated by putting the baby to the breast almost immediately after delivery, and on reflection this seems eminently reasonable. The tonic effect on the uterine muscles of the infant suckling causes the contractions to continue while the uterus is in an active state. If suckling is delayed for twelve to twenty-four hours, blood from the more flaccid resting uterus oozes into the uterine cavity and contractions are spasmodic and irregular.

One mother of four speaks of no after-pains with the first two children and the last because they were each put to the breast shortly after delivery. With the third child, however, there was a precipitate labour and she remembers hearing the child sucking vigorously at its thumb while she was still in the labour room, but she was drowsy from an anæsthetic and did not see the baby until the next morning. During the night after delivery she lay alone in a single room, without a bell, and experienced severe and distressing pain, which, on looking back, she says was certainly accompanied by anxiety. She thinks that the pain was probably caused by anxiety about herself and the infant.

A district nurse in charge of a large ante-natal clinic near Barnsley, England, when asked to report on this matter replied (30/1/49) : ' I consulted the midwives re your question and they both say after-pains are a thing of the past. The mothers do not complain of after-pains. I don't know whether this is due to the improved conditions, more ante-natal care, or to the fact that there is no pulling and tugging on the towel during the last stage of labour (as was always practised until a few years ago). Ergot tablets are given as routine. The babies are always given to the mothers soon after delivery. The doctor who attends the Ante-Natal Clinic now is of the same opinion.'

Smoking and Breast-feeding

Cigarette smoking is an almost universal modern habit, another symptom of the prevalent anxiety in most people's lives. It is a respectable form of auto-erotic activity, which results from the unsatisfied sensuous needs of the individuals concerned. If a woman is dependent on this form of self-gratification she may entirely miss the far greater pleasure that is to be derived from the more mature experience of suckling an infant. If she herself still needs oral satisfaction plus general sedation, she will not appreciate the sensation of giving to another person—her baby. The two experiences belong to different levels of emotional development. It is a pity not to leave a good thing for a better, and some form of psychotherapy may enable her to do so.

37.—THE PSYCHOLOGY OF CHILDBIRTH*
(By M. B.-B.)

Introductory

FOR the first four meetings of 1947 during the months of March and April, the Society was occupied with the psychological problems of childbirth. It is unusual for the Society to devote four consecutive meetings to one subject; but certainly the matter is an important one and interest was well sustained. The fact that some of our active members had

* Sections 37 and 38 on Childbirth appeared in pamphlet form in 1947 and 1948.

recently become, or were about to become, mothers added to this interest. The initiative came from Dr. Enid Cook, who has had a special interest in the subject for some years. She is peculiarly and signally qualified to speak on such a subject. She is a physician who has had considerable experience in ante-natal clinics; she has trained for some years in psychological medicine and is now practising as a medical psychologist; *and* she has three children of her own, now adolescent. Her report (which follows), about the nature and circumstances of the birth of her children, is of great value.

Two propositions or theses were proposed at these meetings:

(1) That childbirth under normal conditions is not necessarily painful.

(2) That it is desirable for the welfare of both child and mother that the mother be conscious and not narcotized at the time of birth of the child.

In view of current obstetric doctrine and practice both theses are arresting. It was intended to publish a summary of these meetings. Since this decision to publish was made, however, there has appeared in *Readers' Digest* of May, 1947, a summary of Grantly Dick Read's book, *Revelation of Childbirth*. This summary in the *Digest* appears to us to be very good and valuable, and has our entire approval. To some extent, however, it has forestalled us in that it contains much of the evidence and contentions that were advanced at our meetings. On the other hand, it may lighten our task in that the *Digest* has a wide circulation and will help therefore to arouse interest in the subject. Also our special concern is the more specifically psychological aspect of the subject.

I (Contribution by Enid F. Cook)

My latent interest in this subject was stimulated recently by a mother nearing her confinement date. Returning from a visit to her doctor, she had called in to see me, a little indignant at his attitude to the approaching event. The nurse had said, 'We will look after you in plenty of time. You will know nothing about it until it's all over.' The doctor had explained nothing to her, and she had left with a sense of deprivation and annoyance. 'Why shouldn't I understand what's going on; I want to go through with this experience;

it's *my* baby, why should they take charge of everything and do me out of my show?' What was happening here? In brief, she was approaching the climax of her biological and psychological development, the supreme moment of a woman's life when she is able to reproduce her kind. And other people were crowding in to remove all responsibility. This started a whole train of thought and feeling in my mind, and ideas crystallized which had hitherto been unexpressed but deeply felt.

By the continued administration of anæsthetics or analgesics in natural childbirth we miss—it seems to me—the great importance of the psychological effect of 'the greatest of all female pleasure-pain experiences,' that is, spontaneous delivery of the infant.

Apart from the effect on the child, whose emotional state at the moment of separation from the mother may colour the whole of its future well-being, the woman herself is deprived of an invaluable experience if she is not allowed an active part in delivery.

With some diffidence I offer my own experience, because it seems to be rare in this generation, but was undoubtedly a natural, satisfying and maturing experience. How do women become emotionally mature? Is it by experiencing and mastering emotions, or by suppressing and avoiding them? Fear undoubtedly plays a large part in the pain and tension associated with childbirth, and if we can indicate the factors which produce fear we may contribute something to the happiness of the race.

My first two children were born in Japan, in our own home, without drug or anæsthetic. My husband was my close companion during the whole pregnancy and present at the actual delivery. There were no disturbing pre-natal events, no anxious relatives, a leisurely and happy pregnancy with adequate understanding of what was taking place, and an active normal existence.

The actual labour began a week earlier than was expected on both occasions and was conducted by an efficient Japanese nurse with whom I could hardly converse, but whose cheerful, confident attitude was reassuring. The first onset of contractions produced a feeling of anticipation—'Here we are at last—something's really going to happen,' and the usual increased activity before any event. Nature provides a lowering of self-consciousness during the second stage of labour, so that one's whole concentration is upon the business of helping the child out. In between the contractions a relaxed and resting period is perfectly provided. It is then that one is thankful to be in one's own bed in peaceful, familiar surroundings, preparing for the next ' round '; it is then that one is most suggestible and aware of atmosphere, grateful for competent assistance and a sense of inevitability—' let it happen.' Looking back, I have no memory of pain such as I can recall resulting from an acute otitis media (earache) four years before marriage. So that comparing the two experiences, the otitis was acutely painful, whereas labour was strenuous but not acutely painful.

The actual birth is a unique experience of which I wouldn't have missed one second. It is the culmination of nine months' preparation, giving one a sense of completeness. As soon as the child is born one has an indefinable sense of achievement quite unlike any other experience. Having him in one's arms to cuddle as soon as he is washed and dressed gives a deep pleasure and satisfaction which produces a tonic effect on the uterus, so that there is much less likelihood of postpartum hæmorrhage, and the child starts life with a sense of security and nearness to the mother that is invaluable. At the second confinement the doctor was not present, and my husband affirms that far from experiencing acute pain I was attempting to direct the Japanese nurse, and there was no evidence of mental or physical distress.

Let us examine more closely the factors involved in such a spontaneous delivery. Fear was reduced to a minimum by:

1. Education.
2. Attitude.
3. Segregation.
4. Peaceful, familiar surroundings.
5. Companionship.

1. *Education*: I had been taught the biological facts of childbirth in the detached atmosphere of a classroom. I had no time as a child or adolescent to listen to horrific tales of the woes and miseries of childbirth. Thus I defeated the first great enemy and fear-promoting factor—ignorance.

2. *Attitude*: All my life I had looked on motherhood as the ideal state for a woman and had practised mothering on dolls and brothers and whatever small children came my way.

3. *Segregation*: At a very suggestible period of my life I was delivered from the infection of my mind by relatives and neighbours. I was immune from the countless adverse suggestions and half-truths of hearsay and idle gossip.

4. *Peaceful, Familiar Surroundings*: It was a domestic event in an ideal environment. There was no separation from the child for the first year, but above all, the maturing experience of having endured the stress and adventure of childbirth without interference. (Animals get away from crowds in order to have their young in peace.)

5. *Companionship*: There was companionship available whenever I needed it, especially at the onset of labour, which is the time above all when a cheerful, confident husband can mean so much to a woman. There was no rushing in a taxi to a strange place, among strange people; it was a domestic affair in familiar surroundings, but without a bevy of anxious relatives and neighbours such as I have seen in poor homes in England. But even with such drawbacks as moaning mothers, there is much to be said for domiciliary midwifery. The science of obstetrics has advanced rapidly with the introduction of anæsthetics, but it has dealt with the *mechanics* of reproduction, ignoring the person involved, whose attitude can be so profoundly affected by those concerned with her condition. It is possible to be very lonely in a *crowd*. Therefore, loneliness is a sense of isolation and increases fear and tension. From women undergoing spontaneous childbirth Dr. Grantly Dick Read has collected plenty of evidence which corroborates my statements. Women who in many cases had previously experienced anæsthetised and unsatisfactory first deliveries, are emphatic that under Dr. Read's care and instruction they were able to face and master fear, thereby experiencing an infinitely more acceptable childbirth.

By contrast with the first two pregnancies, the third confinement in England was the least enjoyable, precisely because some of the factors enumerated above were altered. I was in the zone of criticism from family and friends, who commented on the unfashionable rate at which I was producing children. Again the baby came early, but this time I had to be moved

117

to a small nursing home and so I experienced that sense of isolation and anxiety about getting there in time. This produced tension and a wave of fear as a result, and pain was experienced. As the head was about to be born I felt I could not bear the ordeal, and asked for a whiff of chloroform, which was given. I can well remember the sense of relief which followed a few inhalations of the anæsthetic, but it was my anxiety which was relieved, and I again experienced the sensation of self-emptying which is so distinctive of the birth process. This cannot be classed as pain in the sense in which earache or a sprained ankle is painful to me.

II (By M. B.-B.)

For generations past there has been a common belief that childbirth is a painful, if not very painful process for the mother, and therefore to a varying degree an experience to be feared. (Less attention has been paid to the question whether it is painful or fear-exciting to the baby.) In her addresses and in this report Dr. Enid Cook is propounding the thesis that childbirth is not naturally or inevitably painful to the mother in the absence of any anæsthetic. She bases this thesis partly on her own personal experience and partly on Dr. Grantly Dick Read's book. At the same time she offers another proposition ' that it is desirable in the psychic interest of both mother and child that the mother should be " conscious " and not narcotized at the time of the birth of the child.' She desires that these two theses be taken together in relationship to one another.

Now there appears to be a general tendency to suppose that a belief widely held for thousands of years is probably correct. This seems very doubtful logic; and there are many beliefs thus supposed true for thousands of years that have proved false. If it can be demonstrated that labour and parturition are not necessarily painful without anæsthesia, it is surely a matter of great importance. In the first place it can be stated as a generalization that the performance of all physiological, biological or natural functions in a healthy individual is associated with pleasure, satisfaction or enjoyment, e.g., eating, drinking, sucking, defaecation, micturition, sleeping, muscular activity, rest, are associated with intense pleasure in childhood; relatively less intense in adults; and in adults must be added the enjoyment of the act of conjugal union. Childbirth must presumably be regarded as a physiological function, and not (normally) a pathological one. If then, it is necessarily painful, it is a notable exception to the generalization.

Evidently it is not profitable to investigate or discuss the problem without considering the larger problem of *pain*—its nature, cause and significance. Though we cannot here deal with this problem with any completeness we shall not evade it altogether. Clearly pain is a subjective experience; the only pain we can have direct knowledge of is our own pain; one cannot observe it directly in any one else. We can observe apparent signs or effects or reports of pain in others, and we attempt to assess the nature and severity of the pain by reference to our own reactions—but this is difficult; people vary considerably in their reactions to painful experience. Sometimes a person complains of pain without exhibiting what we regard as the usual signs of pain, but we are not entitled to say that he or she is not suffering pain. Similarly, when Dr. Cook reports that she did not experience pain in circumstances where most women report pain, we are bound to accept her statement. These and other phenomena suggest that pain is partly at least a subjective interpretation of an experience; that the same experience may be interpreted and reported as painful by one subject, and not painful (or perhaps pleasurable) by another. Similarly in hysteria very severe bodily pains are often reported by the sufferer, which cannot be accounted for by any bodily disease. We may easily be deceived by the apparent signs and manifestations of pain. In childbirth, for example, a woman may exhibit groaning or crying, which we are accustomed to associate with severe pain, but she may afterwards report that she suffered no pain, or may even assert this at the time. (The reverse must also be assumed.) But we cannot easily dispose of the view that the groaning or crying indicates some kind of distress, though this be not described as pain. It should be noted here that Dr. Cook does not suggest that labour and childbirth are free from any kind of distress, but only that actual pain is not necessary.

From the point of view of physiology and medicine pain is regarded as resulting from the stimulation of various peripheral sensory organs or nerve endings, conduction by afferent nerves and tracts, and final interpretation in the cerebral cortex. This type of pain is called sensory pain, or pain of sensation, by the psychologist, who regards it as only one of the experiences which he includes in pain. He distinguishes between pain as sensation and pain as total feeling-tone, i.e., a total psychic state. A total feeling-tone may include in it some pain as sensation, but yet be felt as pleasurable because of some other accompanying satisfaction. The sensory pain here is subordinate to, or overwhelmed by, the dominant feeling-tone of satisfaction or pleasure. The sensory pain may, in certain circumstances, even enhance the total feeling-tone of satisfaction or pleasure (see later under *masochism*). As examples of the total feeling-tone are:

(1) A man exerting an intense and sustained muscular effort towards some achievement, as in athletics, rowing, wrestling or mountaineering.

(2) A woman intensely desiring to achieve the birth of her baby.

This mixture of sensory pleasure and pain in total feeling-tone of either pleasure or pain is commonly recognized, and is suggested in common speech. The individual is said to ' forget ' or be ' unconscious ' of pain. But pain presumes consciousness; if a person is unconscious of pain there is no pain.

Poets tend to dwell on this theme: ' Our sincerest laughter with some pain is fraught ' (Shelley). The relation between pain as sensory experience and a total feeling-tone of pleasure or satisfaction is nowhere better illustrated than in the disposition known as *masochism*. And masochism is clearly of great relevance to our present subject. Masochism, like its opposite, sadism, is sometimes regarded solely as a rather unpleasant kind of perversion. This is a misapprehension. Many or most people have some sadism or masochism (sometimes both) in their make-up; when duly integrated and harmonized with other elements in the personality they are both valuable components of character. Masochism has been defined as a tendency to derive sensuous or ' sexual ' pleasure or satisfaction through the experience of inflicted pain. I am not alone in believing this definition misleading in emphasis. I consider that the essential experience which

120

leads to pleasure or satisfaction is described by words such as surrender, submission, self-abasement, being overpowered; experience of sensory pain may be involved as incidental. If such a tendency be over-accentuated and unbalanced, the essential experience may be then described as degradation or humiliation. This may amount to a perversion, i.e., where the degradation is the sole object of desire. Though both sadism and masochism may occur in either sex, sadism is more commonly present in men and masochism in women. Clearly these masochistic tendencies towards surrender, self-effacement, self-abnegation and passivity, are potentially very valuable to a woman as a mother, not only at childbirth, but in the subsequent nurture of the child. It is necessary to remember that fulfilment of these tendencies is associated with pleasure or satisfaction, and *not, normally*, with any flavour of 'martyrdom' or self-sacrifice.

If we allow, as we must, that a masochistic tendency may include the capacity to derive satisfaction or 'pleasure' through the experience of sensory pain, then its value will be specially enhanced here. At this point we reach the kind of difficulty regarding words that we envisaged at the beginning. Commonly, pleasure and pain are regarded as antithetical—here in masochism it seems at first sight as if they were equivalent. This is almost certainly a false assumption. The painful experience contributes to the total feeling-tone of pleasure; that is not to say that the pain itself is pleasure. Also we should note that the painful experience concerned here does not occur in isolation, but in association with a total situation involving a relationship to another person, i.e., it is a part of, or incidental to, the satisfaction of a primitive instinctual urge. But it seems to me that the further examination of this masochistic attitude is not completely accessible to intellectual or logical analysis. To make this possible would require that the terms 'pleasure' and 'pain' have a clear definition acceptable to everyone; and this condition cannot be fulfilled. Thus the matter is more likely to be understood by women who will have a direct and intuitive understanding of masochism than by men, who normally proceed by the more ponderous method of intellect and logic. Furthermore, the women will have great difficulty in explaining the matter to men by verbal communication.

121

At one of the discussions one of the women members made the following statement: ' I have had five children, and had the pleasure of having had one spontaneous delivery; I assure you that the birth process was most painful; but I would not have missed it for anything.'

It appears that answers to the question ' Was childbirth painful to you? ' are (1) ' Yes ' and (2) ' No ' and (3) ' I don't know and it does not matter, because the dominating mental state was one of intense satisfaction.' Interpreting these in the light of the previous discourse:

(1) The total feeling-tone is that of pain; some emotional influence is interfering with the natural functioning of the maternal reproductive tendencies; the conflicting emotional influences almost certainly include *fear*; fear is itself painful and also will interfere with the muscular birth process tending to cause spasm and sensations of pain which in the total psychic state will be in the focus of consciousness.

(2) and (3) Total feeling-tone is pleasure or satisfaction; fear is presumably absent; the maternal reproductive instinct is not interfered with by conflict, but is in harmonious accord with the personality as a whole.

The woman's answer ' I don't know and it does not matter ' (to the question *re* pain or no pain), is liable to be irritating to men who demand a precise answer, ' yes ' or ' no.' To the woman, the question seems rather silly and irrelevant in view of the total feeling-tone of intense satisfaction. A possible masculine analogy could be found if we imagine a man engaged in an important competitive wrestling bout being asked during a period of intense stress whether he was feeling any pain. If he answered at all it would probably be in some profane manner protesting at the interruption of his concentration.

Dr. Cook does not say that her third experience was more painful than the other two, but that the third was *less enjoyable*. She is emphatic that the distress which she felt was due to anxiety and not to pain.

We must assume, however, that *if* pain as sensation becomes extreme or severe, it would in most cases dominate the field of consciousness and produce a painful feeling-tone. This would be as true of the wrestler as of a woman in childbirth.

Theory tends to suggest that under ideal conditions childbirth should be for a woman the supreme sensuous experience. Some women from categories (2) and (3) report that their own experience supports this theory. For them, childbirth was the supreme sensuous experience. The intense satisfaction, pleasure and enjoyment reported here are evidently due to the satisfaction of a strong desire, conscious and unconscious, and the fulfilment of a primary, possibly the supreme primary, function.

THE SOURCES OF LOVE AND FEAR

Parturition involves the muscular mechanism of the genital tract, with active contraction of muscles in the uterus and complete relaxation, and also active dilatation of muscles surrounding the passage. This relaxation and dilatation will be greatly facilitated by a psychic attitude of surrender, passivity and yielding, and will be hindered by any kind of self-assertive tendency, and especially by self-protective mechanisms associated with *fear*. Of fear more will be said later. The vagina has been observed to dilate spontaneously to an open cavity or tube of three inches in diameter without any passive stretching by any object or instrument. Three inches is approaching the dimensions of a baby's head, and only about one inch need be allowed for passive stretching. This spontaneous dilatation, though muscular, is part of the mechanism of relaxation referred to above. It will occur only in a psychic state from which fear is absent and instinctual desire is free and dominant. The tube or passage through which the baby passes from the uterus to the exterior is formed of the lower part or neck of the womb and the vagina. This tube is enveloped in muscles (most of which are involuntary). One group of these constricts the tube, and the other dilates it. In parturition a peristaltic wave passes down the tube, involving harmonious and rhythmic reciprocity between the two groups of muscles. This will only take place smoothly and freely in favourable psychic states, and *not* in conditions of fear—conscious or unconscious. In the presence of fear, constriction will dominate and perhaps inhibit relaxation, and tend to close the tube and obstruct the free passage of the baby. Fear has profound effects upon the whole organism, physical and psychic. It fortifies the organism to deal with

the danger by fight or flight, by inhibiting the anabolic processes of digestion and nutrition, and sending blood to the
voluntary muscles, brain, lungs and heart. Its effect on the
genital tract is part of this mechanism. Under primitive conditions it would clearly be highly dangerous to be giving
birth to a child during an attack by wild animals or enemies.
It should be noted that the effect of fear is the same whether
the exciting cause of the fear is some real danger—such as
fire, or attack by animal or foe—or whether it be a bogey
of one's own imagination.

If there is fear then, the process of birth will be obstructed;
there will be spasm or constriction instead of relaxation and
dilatation, and this disturbance will cause sensations of pain.
An analogy in miniature is afforded by dysmenorrhoea (painful menstruation). A very large proportion—probably 90
per cent. of dysmenorrhoea in young women—is psychic in
origin and cause, and can be treated successfully by psychotherapy. A similar mechanism is involved. Instead of the
free extrusion or ' birth ' of menstrual material. emotions of
a negative character, particularly fear, shame and disgust,
interfere with the rhythm of the mechanism and cause spasm,
obstruction and pain. Moreover, sensations are interpreted
as painful which in a healthier subject are interpreted as
pleasurable. If the birth process, then, is accompanied by
fear, the process may be presumed to be pain-producing. As·
was indicated earlier, since childbirth is assumed to be
necessarily painful, the majority of women will therefore
fear it. If they fear it, the process will presumably be painful
and their fears will be realized. We are contending here that
if this fear could be dissipated, and confidence and happy
anticipation substituted, pain would be absent (under normal
conditions). What would then replace it would not just be
' freedom from pain,' but a feeling-tone of intense satisfaction. In his book Dr. Read seems to demonstrate that, given
the right conditions this can be done in practice.

This leads us to another human trait which is more marked
usually in women than men—suggestibilty. This suggestibility is related to masochism, and involves emotional dependence.

Obviously, women (like men) vary in their degree of
emotional dependence. but it is certainly true that the depen-

dence and suggestibility of a woman is greatly intensified in the later stages of pregnancy and in labour. This is biologically natural and necessary, as in the primitive state a woman in this condition would be very vulnerable to enemies unless protected. Just as, therefore, she becomes more dependent and suggestible at this time, so she will readily respond to the right kind of support, reassurance and encouragement. This process then can be used to eliminate fear. And it is absurd to expect a woman to face pregnancy and labour without a full measure of support and encouragement from her entourage, especially her husband and her family, as well as the medical attendants. Too often the reverse condition exists, where she is deprived of adequate support, bothered by anxious friends and relatives, and assailed by harrowing tales of possible disasters.

We now come to an aspect of the subject which is of special concern to us. Pregnancy, labour and childbirth are part of the reproductive process, and the beginning of parenthood. It will be agreed that parenthood is an adult function. Biologically we can divide the course of life into two phases: (1) childhood, where the individual needs adult parents and is physically and psychically dependent on them; (2) adulthood, where the individual (a) has no further need for parents as such; (b) has a need for fulfilment in reproduction and the protection of another individual (baby or child). This is obvious. What is not so obvious is that many people grow up and develop physically into an adult bodily form, but fail to do so psychically, i.e., in emotional development. Psychically and emotionally they remain children more or less, and consciously or unconsciously need parents to protect them. They are physically mature and psychically immature. though their intellectual attainments may be above the average. It will be evident that such people are biologically qualified to become parents, but not psychologically qualified. They are not adequate to the task of human parenthood and nurture. What is required for adequate human parenthood is *emotional maturity*. To be emotionally mature means the same thing as to be mentally healthy. Three criteria of this condition might be mentioned here.

(1) Confidence in the capacity to deal with one's own

life and also to protect another person (e.g., a child) as well.

(2) Capacity to love (objectively) another person.

(3) Subordination of egoistic and self-preservative tendencies.

This condition of emotional maturity has a peculiar relevance to childbirth. To an emotionally mature person childbirth will be anticipated with eagerness and satisfaction as a fulfilment; and since egoistic and self-preservative tendencies are subordinated or submerged in the intense interest in the new life, fear will not arise.

On the other hand, the emotionally immature person is *ex hypothesi* unprepared for and inadequate to, the experience, and accordingly is likely to approach it with anxiety. Unfortunately, it must be stated that in our culture many people of both sexes who are biologically adult and who marry and are given in marriage, are emotionally immature. The problem of Mental Health or Emotional Maturity is wide and urgent.

Dr. Cook has paid particular attention to the desirability of the mother being conscious at the time of the birth of her child. Here again the witness of mothers is very valuable, and the meditations of men not very profitable. There is evidence, however, to suggest that the conscious achievement of birth and its realization sets the seal on emotional maturity.

Among contributions from women to the discussion there were some that had the following tenor:

'Yes, we understand and appreciate all this. You may be right. We can see that it might be very much in the interests of the baby and perhaps in our own best interest if we were conscious at the time of birth. But we are *not* emotionally mature, and do not think this is our fault. You cannot expect this of us; it is too much; we are not heroines.'

This attitude is very reasonable *if* it be true that childbirth is necessarily and totally painful. There is a psychological 'law' which states that by nature we are compelled to seek pleasure and avoid pain. But we are contending here that this point of view is based upon (1) irrational fear, (2) misapprehension. It implies that this form of childbirth (natural and without narcotics) represents a heavy demand or obligation for the mother.

126

We are suggesting here that the opposite is the truth—that it represents an opportunity for satisfaction and a privilege available to them if they will take it. And emotional immaturity can be treated.

If our contentions are sound, an important practical conclusion follows: It is that in the absence of gross physical abnormality the most important element in treatment or management of labour is psychological care, and this is much more important than mechanical or physical management.

38.—PSYCHOLOGICAL PREPARATION FOR CHILDBIRTH

I (By Enid F. Cook)

In *The Psychology of Childbirth* I referred to the desirability of the mother being conscious at the time of delivery of her child. I have been asked to give reasons for this statement, as it runs counter to current practice in New Zealand. I also feel that it is extremely important that mother and child should be kept together in the early weeks of the child's life and not separated as they are in the nursing homes and hospitals of this country.

We are familiar with the emphasis on the need for security in the child's environment, and of the part played by the mother in providing this security. We know that a sense of security is achieved by adequate mothering. We also know that this is felt by the infant long before he can make his needs known except by crying.

Adequate mothering means the presence of a familiar person, and there is no other person quite as satisfying as one's own mother. This being so, how reprehensible and damaging it must be to remove the new-born infant out of sight and hearing of the mother when he is at his most helpless and instinctive level. The first need is for the comfort and reassurance of the breast. But if the mother is drugged and unconscious, how can she supply that need? If an infant is put to the breast soon after delivery, not only is the maternal tone improved and maternal feelings stimulated, but the child feels safe and the proximity of the mother compensates for the loss of intra-uterine security.

If his dependent and sensuous needs are met by a mother

who is there whenever he needs her, and who enjoys him as he feeds, all will be well. The physical act of sucking the breast is accompanied by intense satisfaction, often shown by grunts and eventual rosy repletion, but this satisfaction is intimately connected with the fact that mother is sharing his pleasure. Anyone will endorse this who has observed the wailing, anxious infant who at feeding times noses frantically round and finally fastens on the nipple and begins to suck as if his life depended on it—as indeed it does. It is not only milk he is seeking, but the reunion with the mother and the feeling of safety and comfort, which this process brings. This is what 'feeling loved' implies—'a presence of someone who knows my need.' He will soon learn to smile his appreciation of her, and to thrive because he is safe and comfortable. The smaller the infant, the greater is this need and the less able is he to express it.

After nine months of gestation the sudden transition into a loud bright world of separate existence is in itself a shock. So we need to bear this in mind, and endeavour to keep the child in close association with the mother, whose feelings can best interpret the child's need. Maternal instinct, if allowed to function and not frustrated, will respond to the child's cry, and so his anxiety is allayed, but a child left to cry alone is in serious danger of feeling abandoned and therefore panic-stricken.

An infant made anxious by such treatment will not thrive so well, is liable to develop digestive upsets and is more vulnerable to infection. Some English hospitals, notably the conservative Queen Charlotte Maternity Hospital, are discovering the physiological value of having the baby in a cot beside the mother's bed during the first two weeks of life. Babies will not get 'windy spasms' if they are not made anxious by an untimely separation. They are handled by one mother instead of by a succession of busy nurses on eight-hourly shifts. Above all, the mother becomes more competent and experienced in handling her child from the beginning, and there is not the disturbing change-over when she has to return home. She is responsible for her child from the first, but she should have expert supervision and help if it is required.

Suppose a woman's maternal feelings are inhibited, as they so frequently are, by fear and uncertainty? Or is the modern woman so developed intellectually that her natural feelings are warped and stifled? If so, it is certainly an indictment of our modern culture, where such stress is laid on intellectual attainments, and the importance of emotional maturity is ignored. The most successful mother is one whose own infancy was satisfying and secure. As an infant her sensuous feelings were focussed on her mouth, but as development proceeds these pass to more general areas, and the mother who can enjoy the sensuous pleasure of breast-feeding is passing on to her child the joy of living and sense of well-being which is an indefinable source of vigour.

Childbirth should be, of course, the happy culmination of a happy courtship and marriage, so that the man has an important part to play in the development and encouragement of his wife's emotional life. The sense of security and satisfaction can better develop in the woman if the husband is enjoying and supporting his wife, making no undue demands upon her during pregnancy, but seeking to contribute to her well-being and peace of mind.

The period of pregnancy can be one of real fitness and pleasurable anticipation when the woman, instead of feeling that her freedom is curtailed, can prepare with eagerness for a new chapter which will be one of the highlights of her experience. To quote Helene Deutsch:* ' If the disturbing elements within and without are well mastered, if the delivery follows a normal, natural course, and if by direct emotional influence or other means the excess of fear and pain is successfully reduced, childbirth is the greatest and most gratifying experience of woman, perhaps of human beings. Two powerful factors make it so; first, the joy in accomplishment that is connected with the mastering of fear and pain and with the woman's own activity: second, the *happy relation with the child*† that begins immediately after delivery. The dynamism of this relationship is clear; the whole psychic energy tied to the labour and withdrawn from the outside world streams towards the child in the moment of delivery, and the newly achieved freedom from pain and fear creates a feeling of triumph and endows the first moment of motherhood with real ecstasy. It is not yet motherliness that char-

* *Psychology of Women*, Vol. II, p. 248.
† Italics are ours.

acterizes the mother-child relationship—it is only the first foundation stone, perhaps even a reservoir from which springs the gradually developing love for the child.'

If childbirth is ' the greatest and most satisfying experience of women,' surely the omission of this conscious achievement may have some effect upon the mother, whose lot it should be to enjoy her children. Are we, by failure to appreciate the significance of such an occasion, crippling our mothers emotionally and depriving them of a maturing experience which would fit them for adequate motherhood? If, as is unquestionably shown by psycho-analytic experience, it is the instinctive response of mother love that the child most needs, how can we foster the maternal feelings in the mother? Observation of newly-born animals is instructive—the cat begins licking its kittens and doubtless by this instinctive act develops her maternal feelings towards the offspring. Experimental work with African bucks has shown that if the mother is unaware of the delivery of the baby and does not lick it, she fails to develop the usual interest.* A biologist observing the birth of a calf notes that the licking by the cow stimulates and invigorates the calf, until it staggers to its feet and finally stumbles against the body of the mother and nuzzles its way to the teat. Thus the sensuous act on the part of the mother develops her own maternal interest and awakens the calf to an awareness of her presence and his own sensuous need which is satisfied by the act of sucking. The same process is observable in sheep and other mammals.

I would suggest that a similar sensuous stimulus in the human relationship is desirable and beneficial to both mother and child. The licking of the animals is replaced by early fondling and nursing of the child. It is noteworthy that Dr. G. D. Read† passes the newborn child to the mother as soon as possible after the birth. His remarkable success is due not only to the *physiological* benefit resulting from the woman's interest and active participation in the birth, but to the *psychological* stimulation of maternal feelings which this action effects. H. Deutsch‡ states that the transfer of emotions from

* E. Marais: *The Soul of the White Ant.*
† *Revelation of Childbirth*; Read.
‡ *Psychology of Women.* Vol. II, p. 245.

the woman's own ego to the child as the object is prepared even during the act of birth. That means that she ceases to be concerned about her own discomfort, and having mastered her fears, can find delight and satisfaction in the new life that she has brought to birth. She begins to live for a child begotten as the result of a love relationship. She was loved for herself by the husband—this love was expressed in coitus, a taking-in of another's germ plasm. The expulsion of the child is the natural culmination of this process, biologically and psychologically, and should be experienced with all the awareness possible to the individual woman. There are certainly many women to whom coitus is painful and fear-producing, but one cannot regard this state as normal or desirable. Would anyone consider anæsthesia a suitable remedy? Why then should a flight into unconsciousness on account of fear be considered the correct treatment of the act of childbirth? On the contrary, one woman spoke of her feelings of 'shame and degradation' as she recovered from the anæsthetic after her firstborn. 'We are not educated; we don't even know how to have our own children' was her reaction.

In some women there may be an enjoyment of coitus but a paralysing fear of pregnancy and its consequences. This implies a fear of losing oneself, of having to be responsible for another life than one's own. Such women may dread the threat to their intellectual life, or fear that they will no longer be attractive and vivacious, and therefore may not retain the admiration of their husbands. Ante-natal treatment should be directed to a modification of this narcissistic attitude, and needs to include some education of the husband, in order that he may comprehend the nature of the conflict in his wife's mind. In most women, conscious or unconscious fear of some kind is the factor that requires dealing with during pregnancy. Frequently it is heightened by uncomprehending attendants. It is useless to say, 'Don't be frightened.' The question is rather, 'Of what are you afraid, and why?' The fear is more likely to be unconscious, and to be exhibited in symptoms such as headache or sleeplessness. It is not enough to treat the symptom. Skill is required to bring the real trouble into consciousness, so that it can be dealt with.

131

The conclusions we reach, therefore, are:

(1) A woman will desire to be conscious during the birth of her child if she is not afraid.

(2) This will provide the child with her natural protection when he most needs her, and will lessen anxiety with its attendant evils.

(3) Ante-natal preparation involves time spent in understanding and unravelling the emotional conflicts arising in the woman, so that she may be psychologically ready for motherhood. It is worse than useless to hand her a printed pamphlet including the admonition, ' Do not worry, it may do harm.' Time and patience are required to trace the source of the worry, which will be lessened by this very process of listening and simple education on the part of the medical attendant.

(4) The woman must have someone to whom she can talk with confidence and of whom she can ask questions as they arise during the pregnancy. She must learn to face and master fear by verbalizing her emotions. Vomiting of pregnancy can in most instances be dispelled by adequate understanding on the part of practitioner and patient. It is usually a symptom of unconscious anxiety which will therefore be connected with some early emotional conflict.

(5) Detailed instructions should be given about the process which is taking place, so that she may understand new sensations which arise and note her reaction to them. The first movements may thus be anticipated, and the position of the child understood with interest. The physiology of labour and the purpose of contractions can be comprehended by most women and thus an attitude of co-operation fostered. If there are other children they can be included in the family secret, when the mother herself is happy about the pregnancy. Pregnancy is also the period when the mother can learn something in advance about the psychological needs of the infant in addition to preparing garments and gadgets. Ante-natal instruction could well include literature on the importance of the first five years.

(6) The woman needs moral support throughout pregnancy and most of all during labour. To be put into a strange room alone and told to ' get on with it ' leaves one with a sense of being deserted in a crisis. Some women prefer their husbands at such a time and they should be allowed this companionship which is the ideal one if the man is equal to his responsibility. Failing him, and understanding familiar friend is desirable, but the woman should not be left to face the unknown alone.

(7) It is said, ' Why not avail yourself of the benefits of science? Anæsthetics are a boon to mankind, why suffer unnecessarily? ' Those who say this fail to see that contractions are not necessarily pain-producing if there is no fear and tension. What is of far greater importance is the close association of pleasure and pain in feminine personality* and the amazing suggestibility of the pregnant woman. Herein lies a wealth of possibility for the mature and confident attendant who can inspire the patient with courage, help her to realize her highest hopes and dispel her deepest fears.

* See 37—*The Psychology of Childbirth* (page 113).

II (By M. B.-B.)

It may be asked, since our proper and confessed concern is with mental health and its attainment, why we enter into a domain which is regarded as belonging to the obstetricians. It is because it is now established beyond dispute that the mental health of an individual depends almost completely on early nurture. In the last analysis the serious and widespread incidence of neurosis in our society is due to a serious failure in motherhood. This is not the same thing as saying that blame should be attached to the large numbers of mothers who fail: many of them have the best of intentions towards the child before and after its birth. The failure is due to ignorance and a combination of unfortunate influences and teaching. In the broad sense it is a failure of education.

The aphorism ' the child must be loved ' means more than can be adequately expressed in words; but part of what it means is that, in the first year of life especially, all his needs must be understood and met, and all his fears appreciated and allayed. This can only be achieved if there is a strong emotional bond between mother and child.

As Dr. Cook points out, in the case of certain other mammals this emotional and sensuous bond is established in the first few minutes following the birth by intimacies such as licking; if this is prevented the mother may refuse to accept and nourish the offspring. It would be reasonable to assume that a similar mechanism exists in humans; and there is evidence to demonstrate its existence. The most convincing evidence of this kind comes from women themselves.

If the mother is anæsthetised and unconscious at the time of birth and for some time afterwards, the baby will be brought to her (perhaps from another room) and '*introduced*' as her baby. Inevitably this baby is something of a stranger. She accepts it as hers on trust. It occasionally happens that a woman recovers from the anæsthetic unaware that her baby has been born.

If on the other hand the woman is conscious at the time of delivery and her instinctive wish to hold the baby immediately afterwards is not frustrated, there is little if any break in the continuity of the relationship. There is evidence to show that this initial experience affects the subsequent feeling-relationship of mother to baby and establishes a bond which is of the greatest importance to the future welfare of the child.

It is not suggested that this conscious state at the time of delivery is the sole determining factor in the mother-child relationship; other conditions are necessary accompaniments: but it *is* suggested that it is a condition of great importance.

We are confronted by the argument that though such conditions may be important for the mental health of the baby it is too much of an ordeal to ask of the mother. We believe this argument to be false and have tried to refute it in the previous chapter of this book. We believe that if the mother is consistently fed with suggestions that the approaching birth is both dangerous and painful, it will certainly be an ordeal for her, and will probably require anæsthesia. In this case she will be deprived of an experience which, as Dr. Enid Cook explains clearly, is the fulfilment of her nature and would provide her with the greatest satisfaction.

Another argument is that in view of all the possible mishaps in labour it is much wiser to have full anæsthesia and thus have the patient under complete surgical control. In reply to this also we think that some of the possible mishaps are promoted by an attitude of apprehension and anxiety, *even with anaesthesia,* and that some of them may be averted by having an adequately prepared, confident, conscious mother in whom there is both appropriate relaxation of certain muscles, and vigorous tone in others.

In the preceding chapter we were concerned with principles, and it is desirable that we should say something about the practical application of these.

It is far from our purpose to suggest that a woman should be invited to undertake labour and parturition without anæsthesia unless careful preparation for the event has been provided. Also we wish to emphasize that we do not recommend this method of childbirth unless a careful physical examination has been made, and any abnormal physical condition excluded which would make the process of labour abnormal or difficult.

It has been the custom for some time to supervise and regulate the physical regime of the woman during pregnancy, but hardly any attention has been paid to the psychic aspects of that period. When one reflects upon this it is rather astonishing, for surely the psychic attitude of the woman to the approaching event is at least as important as the physical. We contend that throughout the whole period of pregnancy there should be sustained support and attention to the psychic aspects. This attention will involve *education* in the broadest sense of the word. Its form will depend to a large extent upon the personality and the degree of emotional maturity of the woman. If, as may often happen, she is emotionally immature and retains some of her childish attitudes, this education will involve some psychotherapy. In effect the purpose is to increase knowledge and self-confidence, to allay fear and replace it by pleasurable anticipation.

This education will also include some instruction concerning the anatomy and physiology of the organs concerned. For example, the vagina is a passage through which the baby passes from the uterus to the exterior. It is supplied with two groups of muscles—one group which constricts it and one group which dilates it. In the functionless state the walls of the passage are kept in apposition by the constrictor group. In the process of birth (under normal conditions) the constrictor group is inhibited and the dilator group comes into operation and actively distends the passage to a diameter of several inches. As the walls of the vagina are also elastic the lumen of the passage may be increased still further by passive stretching by the head of the child.

These anatomical and physiological facts account for some phenomena which frequently perplex uninstructed women. They may observe that the vagina presents a very small orifice and the passage of a finger or a pessary may be felt as painful. How then can it possibly permit the passage of a baby? This is because of the psychic state of the woman at the time, which will include some fear, thus bringing the constricting group of muscles into powerful protective action to close the passage. For similar reasons coitus may be painful, as in vaginismus—a condition which always involves fear.

In the previous chapter it was stated that the vagina had been observed to dilate spontaneously to an open cavity three inches in diameter. This was not in childbirth, and was not produced by any kind of passive stretching. The statement was received with some incredulity in some quarters. The observation was made by the writer, who was also incredulous, but was compelled to accept the evidence of his own eyes. The conditions were no doubt exceptional in that the woman was in a dissociated hysterical state—one in which fear was absent and genital activity completely dominant. The fact that these exceptional psychic conditions were present does not detract from the value of the observation. The same conditions of genital muscles will operate in a woman in a conscious and integrated state if fear is absent and interest in genital function dominant. The observation referred to above is all the more pertinent and remarkable since the woman concerned had suffered from severe vaginismus in her married life. She had, however, borne two children.

In pregnancy the suggestibility of a woman is increased. This state of mind can be used to her advantage, or abused. It is commonly abused by unfortunate mischievous suggestions of danger and mishap, which reduce confidence and pleasurable anticipation, and induce anxiety. It can be used constructively in the way suggested earlier to fortify confi-

dence and reduce or abolish fear. Suggestions to this end may
be made in the full waking state or in a state of relaxation
of any desired degree. Carried to the fullest extent they will
amount to hypnotic suggestions—that is, suggestions given
in a state of semi-consciousness, or even in hypnotic sleep.
In fact there is good reason for the assertion that pregnancy
and childbirth are states in which hypnosis is pre-eminently
indicated as a therapeutic measure. If practice in the technique of relaxation and hypnosis be carried out during pregnancy, then, if circumstances arise which call for anæsthesia,
full anæsthesia can be attained by hypnosis without the aid
of any drug. The great advantage of this is that full consciousness can be restored at any moment, which is not possible if drugs are used.

A doctor with whom I was discussing this said: ' This all
sounds very nice, but it will surely take a lot of the doctor's
time, and therefore be expensive to the patient.' He is
assuredly right in both surmises, and also surely it would be
time well spent. Again it has been said by doctors that this
procedure works very satisfactorily in the hands of Dr.
G. D. Read, because he has a specially suitable personality.
If it were true that he is the only person existing who is
capable of such treatment, then it would be a serious reflection upon the personality of other obstetricians.

Since the publication of our first pamphlet we have
been fortunate enough to find women who were willing to
test the truth of these principles. The results are claimed
both by them and by ourselves to be a verification of these
principles. These confinements took place in the homes of
the women concerned and not in any institution. There is a
reason for this. The staff of obstetrical institutions are
rigidly trained in methods which are so markedly in contrast
to these principles that it is very difficult indeed to attain the
necessary atmosphere. In particular, many of them have a
special nursery in which the babies are segregated and therefore separate from the mother, which renders impossible the
regime which we regard as essential. This regime requires
the baby to be in a cot alongside the mother from the time of
its birth. In addition to other advantages the mother of the
baby will be the boss and have the say as to what is to be

done about the feeding and nursing; and not some official person, however competent.

Another advantage of the home over institutions is that the practice of the latter is not to admit the patient until labour has begun: this is because they tend to be overcrowded and understaffed. This puts the patient in the position of having to reach the hospital quickly enough after labour has begun —which must inevitably cause anxiety; and this is preeminently the state to be avoided. The greater the distance from her home, the more acute this is. If she is in her own home with a familiar midwife in attendance she can take to her bed whenever she feels disposed, and therefore feels secure. Moreover she is in familiar, not strange, surroundings and with familiar people.

For successful results in this matter of natural childbirth a harmonious co-ordinated team is necessary: (1) the mother, (2) the doctor, (3) a midwife, (4) the immediate relations.

As regards the doctor, in certain circumstances where the doctor may be a good obstetrician in the physical sense, but not experienced on the psychic side, it may be desirable to have a physician trained to deal with the psychic side also in attendance. In this case the two would work in co-operation, but the former (the obstetrician) would only actively participate if circumstances required him.

Finally we must add that we are aware that childbirth may be attended with accidents, some avoidable and some unavoidable. The methods of childbirth we have advocated are all contingent upon the assumption that a thorough and competent prenatal examination has been made, to exclude any discoverable pathological condition which may affect labour. Only if such examination indicates that conditions are normal do we advocate the procedure. If a pathological condition is found, we are dealing not with a physiological process, but with one involving pathological features, and we would consider that such a case would be better in a hospital.

39.—EXPERIENCES OF NATURAL CHILDBIRTH

I (By F. E.)

' BECAUSE of what I have learned at the Christchurch Psychological Society, I decided to have this, my fourth baby, at home. Home seemed to be the right place in which to have about me persons who would encourage and be sympathetic with my desire to be conscious of my baby's arrival, and to be able to enjoy her first cry and hold her right away.

' Although the chloroform was handy if I wanted it, everything was organized to help me relax. I knew exactly what was going to happen if I was not frightened, and was also capable of relaxing at the right times. Especially during the last part of the first stage I found a very decided easing in the discomfort of the contractions if I was in a comfortable lying-down position with someone to remind me about the technique in relaxing so the muscles could give more easily and quickly.

' In a very short time the second stage, with its different type of discomfort, was upon me. I didn't want any chloroform, it was over with so soon. Even the periods of relaxation between the extreme effort of pushing (which was automatic, anyway) were short. I gave birth to the biggest baby of my four, 8 lbs. 4 ozs., and her hand was beside her head, too. I had no stitches and felt fine. There had only been a very uncomfortable splitting feeling which certainly was of very short duration and not at all unbearable. I felt quite annoyed at having to wait for them to cut baby's cord before I could see and hold her properly. The bathing had to wait until I had cuddled her. The midwife said it was the most natural delivery she had ever seen.'

II (By M. J. N.)

' I have been a member of the Christchurch Psychological Society for five years and was intensely interested when a paper entitled " The Psychology of Childbirth ' was presented, the fundamental aspect of which was that normal childbirth need not necessarily be painful.

' As soon as I knew I was pregnant, I decided to learn more about these theories, so purchased and studied a book written by Grantly Dick Read which had been referred to at lectures. I also made arrangements to have my baby at home as I am convinced that mother and child should not be separated as is the case in most maternity hospitals. However, I was some time overdue and was getting agitated as the doctor told me that I would have to go to a hospital if labour did not start within a few days. To prevent this, I took a large dose of castor oil which certainly precipitated matters, and in a short time I was experiencing acute discomfort. This discomfort continued, and it was not until some time later that I realized this was actual labour, and then my husband left to collect the midwife.

' As the contractions became more frequent, I realized that they might not return in time and became agitated, whereupon I used an Ethyl Chloride Inhaler which I had been taught to use if needed. It was necessary to do this as I had to instruct my sister in the preparation of the bed. I realized I could not delay my baby's birth much longer so got into bed. As soon as I relaxed the water broke, and with the next contraction the head was born.

' The actual birth of the head was absolutely painless and I am sorry now I was not able to carry out Read's ideas right from the beginning. The baby's hurried arrival caused a slight tear which I am sure would have been avoided had I not taken the castor oil.

' Immediately my baby was born, I raised myself on my elbows and had a good look at her and it was a thrilling moment when nurse laid her in my arms. Her cot was beside mine day and night and thus I was able to comfort and feed her when she needed it. She quickly developed a four-hourly routine. She has been a very contented baby right from the start, and I feel sure this is because she has never been separated from me and knows I shall not fail her.

' I am really enjoying this baby, maybe because I am older and more confident, or maybe I have learnt to put first things first, and am not trying to make the baby conform too much to the routine of the house. It is quite evident she enjoys her feeding; she makes satisfied noises as she sucks, will stop feeding to smile and gurgle with pleasure—so life is good for us both.

140

' My daughters are becoming quite good nurses and I am able to leave her with them for short periods now.

' The birth of this baby, my third and largest of the three, was a most satisfying and maturing experience.'

III (By H. B.)

' As I could not persuade my doctor to co-operate in any degree with my wish to carry out my desire for natural childbirth, and as the nurses at the maternity hospital seemed very sceptical, the external circumstances were far from helpful for my second confinement. Nevertheless, I felt so utterly convinced of the basic truth of the principles underlying the method put forward in Read's *Revelation of Natural Childbirth* that I felt very happy and confident that this birth would be a very different affair from the so-called " normal " birth that I endured with my first child.

' When I arrived at the hospital the beds and theatre were occupied, so I lay on a hard, padded board on the top of the bath for the first stage of labour. Despite this, I was able to relax completely through all but the last two contractions of a six hour first-stage labour. I read on and off during this period, rested, and towards the later stages seemed to doze; all this despite repeated requests by the nurse to get up and walk round the garden as I wasn't " doing anything." My normality in appearance also enabled me to avoid being drugged—a thing I wished at all costs to avoid.

' I experienced my first and only pain after the water broke with a sharp crack because I momentarily became tense and frightened. Then after three sharp contractions (the nurse being utterly amazed that I was at such an advanced stage of labour) I walked down a long passage on to the admission room bed. Although I was perspiring freely, breathing heavily, and feeling sleepily dazed, I felt confident and quite relaxed. Immediately I had my first second-stage contraction and felt the head on my leg. The nurse then insisted on an anæsthetic and held the mask firmly over my face. Evidently things did not go so well after this. The anæsthetic must have been heavy for apparently the baby was not born for some time afterwards. I woke about two hours later still feeling doped, and with an extremely tender and painful

141

stomach. I was told that the baby had a hard time of it and that it took twenty minutes to start the breathing. Vague mention was made of strangling due to a tight cord round the neck. Subsequently I thought what a different story there would have been had there been a quick delivery of an undoped child (even with a tight cord) from a conscious co-operative mother.

' My next child was born at home under comparatively ideal circumstances. Again, we could not get medical co-operation, but this doctor was at least willing to humour me, and allow me to have my way. He was a young doctor, and said that it was my responsibility anyway. However, I had an ideal husband present throughout the birth, and a friendly co-operative midwife—although this was her first experience of this type of birth.

' Unfortunately the head was in an occipito-posterior position and thus I experienced a long first-stage labour of twenty-six hours. During this period, I went to a cinema, had a good night's sleep, attended to my house and children, until about five hours before the birth, when I went happily to bed. I chatted to my husband and nurse and coped well with the contractions until the last hour, when from time to time I had discomfort severe enough to prevent the previous complete bodily relaxation. I also had an unpleasant dull ache in my back, and the lower part of my body was extremely tender and sensitive to touch, and cold. My breathing was heavy and I needed occasional sips of water. During contractions I required *utter* stillness, any movement being most disturbing. This discomfort—amounting at the end of the first stage to painful contractions—was quite unlike this period in my previous birth, and was almost certainly caused by the abnormal position of the baby who was probably turning during this time. When the nurse said that she thought the cervix was fully dilated, I gently " leaned " on a " held breath," timing this just after the climax of the next contraction. The pain in my back was then greatly eased.

' I did this once or twice more, then turned on my back and said, " Look out, chaps. This is it! " (My heels were given a purchase for pushing by towelling stretched firmly across the bed at what would normally be the knee level, and I pulled on my husband's forearm, which he held about a foot above,

142

and across my chest.) Also, I deliberately relaxed completely in the few seconds before the onset of the contraction I could feel was coming.

' As the strong contraction swept over me, I bore down on a large " held breath," and the water broke under the pressure. The baby's head followed immediately. I took a small secondary breath as I felt the head about to crown and bore down gently with a feeling of complete control. I felt a momentary sense of great stretch as the head crowned. Then I took another quick breath and the rest of the baby was born effortlessly. It all happened so quickly, I was hardly aware of the birth till the baby shrieked and my husband called out that we had a baby boy.

' I then had a feeling of extreme nudity and sudden physical chilling. I hardly noticed this, however, as I held my 7 lb. baby (still attached to the cord) and comforted and loved him and felt utterly content and happy in the wonder of it all.

' A minute or so later, the nurse suggested that I give another " push " to see if the placenta was ready. as the cord was already anæmic. This I did, and without so much as a grunt, expelled the complete afterbirth in a matter of seconds. A minute or two later, after the cord was cut. I was given my new son and put him to the breast, where he sucked in no uncertain manner for a full ten minutes.

' Although we had an analgesic apparatus handy, and although all the usual anæsthetics were available. I can honestly say that the thought of using any of them never crossed my mind.

' I felt confident and in complete control throughout the birth, and there was none of that compulsive lack of control that is so often mentioned as a danger when the mother is not under anæsthetic. I could have exerted more or less pressure at will.

' Of course, the joy of being conscious at the actual time of the birth needs no underlining—there is a feeling of elation one could not readily forget.

' It is still uncertain whether or not the head turned to the normal position for the actual delivery: neither my husband nor the nurse could be sure when questioned almost immediately afterwards.

' I was up the next day, and had none of the hangovers of fatigue, exhaustion, or depression so often associated with anæsthetized births. On the contrary, I felt extremely well, strong and happy, with a very contented and much loved wee son.

' It was a great pity that the doctor, who like all sceptics, was in sad need of practical education in the methods of natural childbirth, missed the demonstration. By the time he arrived the baby was fed and asleep!'

40.—EXPLANATION OF DRAWING

THIS is a cartoon drawn by a patient, and represents himself in an analytical session with the author. The patient, incidentally, is a professional cartoonist; hence the form of the picture.

The patient is being asked to reproduce the imagery of a nightmare or terrifying dream that he had a day or two previously. This dream had disturbed his sleep and the disturbance persisted through the following day. In his dream he was confronted by the witch-like figure of a woman who was advancing toward him with an uplifted dagger in her hand. It appeared to him that she intended to strike or pierce him with the dagger. He was terrified at her appearance, especially her eyes, and wanted to escape but felt he could not, because, as well as the terror he felt a kind of horrible fascination in her presence.

It is not my practice to interpret dreams of patients or even to suggest interpretations. I prefer the patient to investigate the dream for himself, my rôle being to provide stimulus, encouragement, and support.

The investigation of this dream required several sessions because of the intensity of the emotions associated with it, the most obtrusive of which was fear. At first he was reluctant to reproduce it at all, but with encouragement was willing to face his fears and contemplate it. To describe in detail the processes by which the significance of the dream became apparent would involve many pages of script covering questions by me and excursions into emotional reactions by him over a period of some hours.

Eventually it became clear to him that the witch-like woman was his mother, the dagger was the projecting teat of a bottle held suspended over his face. She appeared to be intending to make a fierce attack upon him with this as a weapon, as a punishment for his violent and unsatisfied desire for union with her via his mouth. He was terrified in the presence of this attack—felt she wanted to transfix him—even to kill him. At the same time he felt a horrible fascination at the idea of being so pierced or transfixed. This fascination is crucial and the motive of the dream. It is composed as follows:—
(1) The basic intense desire and need for satisfaction and security through a ' copulative ' union with his mother via the breast; this desire has not been satisfied since birth and is of overwhelming intensity. Since normal satisfaction is denied he must accept the next best substitutive satisfaction via his mouth, i.e., by thus being attacked by her with a penetrating and dangerous instrument. (2) Since normal satisfaction is always refused it has become associated with rage towards his mother and screaming of which she obviously disapproves. He is terrified of her disapproving eyes. The basic desire therefore has become associated also with feelings of guilt towards his mother. Therefore there is a desire for punishment by his mother and for reconciliation with her by propitiation and atonement.

Presumably many of us have seen a mother or a nurse rather frantically trying to force a bottle upon a resisting and struggling baby. The motive is based on the view that the baby needs food and ought to be fed whether he seems to want it or not. The mother or nurse assumes that she knows better than the baby what he needs or wants.

Investigation of this dream reveals the situation from the baby's point of view. The mother or nurse believes that she is doing what is best for the child. As the baby has no means of knowing the ' scientific ' methods of feeding he naturally interprets this frantic persistence as a malicious attack.

The known history of this patient indicates that his first weeks of life were tempestuous and distressing, with constant crying and screaming, and that breast-feeding was never established. This experience, reinforced by analogous subsequent experiences in the first few years appears to have distorted permanently his capacity to enter into intimate personal relationships. 145

It may be asked why he was able to draw a quasi-humorous cartoon of the situation when he found it so disturbing to reproduce or contemplate.

Actually, the drawing was not done until the situation was shorn of its excessive terror by comprehension and assimilation. Also it is not intended to be humorous.

I have his permission to publish the drawing with this explanation.

41.—CONCLUSION

What, then, is the conclusion of this matter? For unless this book contribute to a better understanding and practice of child nurture it is of little value. The main conclusion is that we must try to produce a better race of parents than now exists, and better parents than we have been ourselves. 'Good' parents do exist in our generation, of course, but they are in a minority. The first requirement for a 'good' parent is to be emotionally mature. The majority of parents are emotionally immature—that is, they still retain in some respects the emotional attitudes characteristic of children. Therefore their children, lacking real parental affection. themselves also remain emotionally immature when they become adult. We must try to break this vicious circle at as many points as possible by educative methods applied to: (1) Parents with young children, (2) Prospective parents, (3) Adolescents, (4) Educationists and (5) Doctors.

The whole matter cannot be condensed into rules, but rules are not without their value. We have contended that the first year of any individual's life is the most critical for mental health. Concerning the first year, I know of no code of rules as good as that given by Joyce Partridge in her little book, *Baby's Point of View*. I understand that unfortunately this is out of print: otherwise I would recommend everyone interested in the care of children to buy a copy and keep it. Here are Joyce Partridge's rules (quoted by her permission):

(1) Try to recognize before your baby is born that in the matter of sex the chances are even.

(2) Don't be afraid to follow maternal instinct and intuition: in other words, give scope to your love for your baby and don't bring him up by rule of thumb.

(3) Breast-feed your baby.

(4) Never leave a baby alone to cry.

(5) Be as much as possible within earshot of your baby in the early weeks and months of life.

(6) Never in any circumstances scold a baby of whatever age, and never allow anyone else to scold him for wetting or soiling napkins or for wetting or soiling any other place whatsoever.

Joyce Partridge is a first-class psychiatrist, a Fellow of the Royal College of Surgeons (England), and a mother.

I commend her rules to you.

It is the daily lot of the psychiatrist to meet and endeavour to relieve people who have experienced years of disability, ill-health, distress, and often of utter misery, all, or nearly all, of which need not have happened if they themselves and their parents had had more understanding.

There are two highly emotionally-toned words in this connection—'IF ONLY.' 'If only I had come to you ten or twenty years ago. . . .' 'If only my mother and father had understood these things. . . .' 'If only I had understood these things when my children were younger.'

If this little book is able to mitigate in any degree some of this widespread distress it will have fulfilled its purpose.

42.—SUPPLEMENTARY NOTE ON 'EVIDENCE'

SINCE this book was written I have read in the Psychological Bulletin* an article by Dr. Harold Orlansky. In it he seems concerned about the 'extensive bibliography' of published material advocating systems of infant care which he says are produced by 'reasoning from Freudian theory,' and which the authors believe will 'promote the growth of secure and unneurotic personalities.' He appears to take the view that these advocates of mental and emotional prophylaxis are basing their assertions on insufficient evidence. He says 'such statements must be regarded as hypotheses, not facts.' In another passage he says, 'Ribble† has waxed rhapsodic about the importance of adequate "mothering" to the development

* Psychological Bulletin, New York University, Vol. 46, No. 1, Jan., 1949.

of sound personality and organic health.' And again, ' It seems to us, therefore, that Ribble takes too *hysterical* a view of the neonate's organic and psychic resources.'

Dr. Margaret Ribble's findings seem to be largely in accord with mine; e.g., I quote, ' The parents who shrink in horror from the animal side of life, make it impossible for the child to develop the very qualities of intelligence and spirituality that they think they stand for.'*

Since this book deals largely with mental hygiene and infant nurture and in places may appear to be arbitrarily dogmatic, it would also be subject to similar criticism by Dr. Orlansky and others; and therefore it is perhaps desirable to anticipate this. Dr. Orlansky wants more evidence, more objective testing of the opinions offered and statistical verification. In an earlier chapter I have referred briefly to the question of proof. I have much sympathy for Dr. Orlansky in his scepticism and his complaint about lack of evidence in regard to assertions about the effect of early nurture upon personality. No doubt some of the statements made in this little volume will be received with a similar scepticism. I have sympathy with him because when I was younger, thirty years ago, I also was sceptical; in fact, I regarded such assertions (about the effect of infantile experience) as highly improbable assumptions. I have, I think, a little more wisdom now and have had to admit my error and recant. The weight of evidence derived from the last thirty years' experience has compelled me to accept matters that I earlier tended to scoff at. This weight of evidence is overwhelming. But I am not sure that Dr. Orlansky would accept this evidence. Actually it is very difficult to produce evidence which is ' scientific ' in the accepted sense of that word or to produce reliable statistics. The evidence is derived from (1) the treatment of adult and adolescent people suffering from psychoneuroses and allied disorders, and (2) the application of derived principles of mental hygiene to infants and developing children. Dr. Orlansky is especially sceptical about (1) and regards the opinions offered as being based on *deductions* as to infantile experience derived from treatment of adults. It is just here I think that the difficulty and the misconception arise.

* *The Rights of Infants.* by Dr. Margaret Ribble.

It is commonly supposed that in order to follow an analytical method it is necessary for the physician to get the patient ' back ' in time or in memory to infantile experiences, or failing this, to interpret analytical material in terms of such experience. In my view and in my experience this supposition is quite false. In my experience these apparently adult people, as far as their emotional development is concerned, and as far as their capacity for personal relationship is concerned, are still living in the first, second or third year of develop- ment. They still want to be nursed and to suck at the breast, to bite, swallow, devour or destroy it, to attack the person (the mother) who seems to withhold it, and in rage perhaps to destroy her. They are still terrified of the strength of these impulses and feel guilty about them, and terrified of the expected attitude of the mother towards them. They still want to be preoccupied with the sensuous satisfaction of defæcation at the optimum moment, or to drive intense satisfaction in defying the parent figure and refusing to defæcate, etc., etc. But these wishes or impulses are associated with strong emotions of anxiety, guilt or disgust. The patient is not fully conscious or aware of them as such; their recog- nition in consciousness would be to them too humiliating or embarrassing to be tolerable. The task of the physician is to encourage the patient to recognize, realize, tolerate and accept these wishes. At first they can only appear in con- junction with the anxiety, guilt and humiliation with which they are invested. This is the first step towards liberating the impulses from this investing fear and guilt. When, by such a process the wishes or impulses are thus freed from fear and guilt they are able to develop into ´a more mature form which is in harmony with the patient's actual age. It is a remarkable fact that such a development or maturation occurs so quickly after liberation, a matter of days or hours instead of years. This resembles removing a flat stone from a young growing plant such as a bulb as it emerges from the ground, and suggests that there is in the human personality an integrating process making towards health and ' wholth.'

In analytical work I do not use ' interpretation ' in the sense this is used in the orthodox psycho-analytic technique. I think perhaps Dr. Orlansky's scepticism might be more justified if I were to do so. I prefer to encourage the patient to see for himself that he is actually reproducing an infantile experience. By such a method it is not difficult to reproduce the type of situation in which the anxiety and guilt were engendered and in which a parent (usually the mother) is involved. This process, then, is *not* reasoning from Freudian or any other theory but *direct observation* of emotional expression and behaviour of the patient. Apart from the language, this expression and behaviour is obviously infantile. Verbal language also is not always used: it is a language of conduct, expression, and gesture.

The above is a brief indication of the source of the evidence derived from treatment of people suffering from emotional disorders. But it is probable that this evidence will not be acceptable to Dr. Orlansky and the very large number of people who share his scepticism. It depends upon the statements of either the physician or the patient. The physician is assumed to be heavily biassed towards verifying hypotheses which he has preconceived, so that his statements are suspect. There is a great difficulty in regard to evidence offered by the patient: it is not to be expected that anyone, patient or otherwise, will readily lay bare the secrets of his soul to the world even in the interests of science. Moreover, even when he attempts to do so his statements are frequently received with incredulity. (There are, of course, psychological explanations for this incredulity in the minds of the general public.) In this connection, therefore, the article in this volume ' Testimony to Psychotherapy ' is especially valuable. Some weight may be attached to the writer's evidence in that he has had many years' training in science and in strict scientific method. Again, however, Dr. Orlansky and his fellow-scientists will probably contend that this evidence is not scientifically acceptable because it depends upon the statement of two people (physician and patient) and cannot be tested by objective test or experiment under control conditions. This is certainly true. If a third person were present at such a session the evidence would not be forthcoming.

It has been suggested that one should install a recording machine and perhaps a television set in one's consulting-room so that records could be taken. Such a scheme would prove disastrous to the method of treatment. Patients are acutely sensitive to the question of being overheard. Delusions as to wires and radio waves are very common. Confidence in the physician would be destroyed. In any case the essential phenomena here are human emotions and feelings. These are notoriously difficult to assess or measure by orthodox scientific method. In fact, in this matter of human emotional development or disorder we have reached the limits of science and scientific method as hitherto understood. We are applying, or seeking to apply, scientific method to emotions. One of the essential prerequisites to scientific investigation is that emotion must be excluded. Here lies a dilemma. John Macmurray discusses this problem from the philosophical angle with great discernment in *The Boundaries of Science.**

It seems that at present the royal road (perhaps the only road) to understanding the mind and feelings of an infant is by the analytical treatment of adults.† The patient, under the necessary conditions, is able to reproduce and *relive* infantile experiences and translate them into language and gesture which is comprehensible to others. Until we can breed a race of mothers so well-equipped as to be able directly to discern the feelings of infants, it would seem that we shall have to rely on the results of analytical treatment. Occasionally at present one finds such a mother but they are somewhat rare. When one does so meet such a mother her opinions and attitude are in accord with psycho-analytic findings, though she may know little of psycho-analytic theory.

The main contention of this book is that if we can breed such a race of mothers there will be much less need for the laborious, expensive and time-consuming process of analysis.

The other source of evidence or verification I have mentioned is that of applying the principles in practice, i.e., in the nurture of children and observing whether they do in fact work, i.e., prevent emotional disorder and promote mental health. For such a test much time must elapse. One must wait until the infant has reached adult life at twenty or

* *The Boundaries of Science,* by John Macmurray (London: Faber and Faber, 1939).

† Melanie Klein claims to derive confirmation from the analysis of children. Of .this I have no direct experience. It is not essentially different from the treatment of adults in that the children treated have acquired language. Most of the crucial traumata with which analytical treatment is concerned occur in the first two or three years and before the language period.

151

twenty-five before a conclusion can be reached. Moreover, there are difficulties here. It is essential to ensure that the principles are fully comprehended. Intellectual assent to the principles is not enough. It is quite inadequate for a parent to read literature and learn a set of rules as to what he or she should or should not do and assiduously apply these rules. It is a matter of feeling and attitude which must be inculcated by methods which transcend the intellectual.

For example, a difficulty arises from the assumption that breast-feeding is always of the same quality. Dr. Orlansky discusses experiments and statistics relating to 'breast-fed' and 'non-breast-fed' babies. This, I am sure, is fallacious. Breast-feeding varies greatly in quality and value from the point of view of personality development. There are some women, who are so ill-adapted to motherhood, but who attempt to breast-feed their baby from a feeling of duty or other motive, who would do less harm by having recourse to the bottle; unless, of course, they are wise enough in time to be aware of the maladjustment and seek treatment for it. It is most fallacious to assume that because a baby is stated to have been breast-fed for six or nine months that therefore all will be well with him. It is the quality of the relationship in the breast-feeding situation that matters. Much more is involved than nutrition.

There is another fallacy regarding statistical investigations, that is, to regard all infants as equal in temperament or innate endowment, and then to study the effect of various nurtural influences upon them. There is very strong evidence to show that infants vary greatly in innate endowment: some are born 'tough' and resilient, others 'tender' and sensitive. The 'tough' ones will emerge unscathed from all kinds of traumata and faulty nurture, so great is their vitality and robustness. The 'tender' ones will suffer seriously from nurtural conditions by which the 'tough' ones would be unaffected. The two types cannot be distinguished at birth and do not relate to mere physical constitution. Moreover, it would, I think, be wrong to assume that the 'tough' type is more socially valuable than the 'tender.'

I think further that it behoves those scientists (and they are many) who are sceptical and critical about these findings of analytical treatment to devise an alternative scheme of mental hygiene and prophylaxis which can deal effectively with the serious problem of emotional disorder and disability. The problem is urgent. Unless we can reduce the mass of emotional and mental ill-health within a generation or two, we shall, I think, be submerged by races and cultures more primitive, less civilized, less erudite, but in some respects, more human.

In this connection it is interesting to compare the point of view of Dr. Weston La Barre published in the Journal of Mental Hygiene: ' Modern anthropologists are coming around to the point of view of modern dynamic psychiatry—that the essential conditioning of children belongs to the very earliest years of the infant.' (From address presented to Nat. Comm. for Mental Hygiene, New York, Nov. 1948.)

BIBLIOGRAPHY

Baby's Point of View, Joyce Partridge (Oxford Medical).

The Origins of Love and Hate. Suttie (Kegan Paul).

Freedom in the Modern World, John Macmurray (Faber and Faber).

Reason and Emotion, John Macmurray (Faber and Faber).

The Lesson of Okinawa, Dillaway.

The Mother: Agent or Object. I. and J. I. Suttie, Brit. Jrn. of Med. Psychol., 1932-1933.